HEATH
MIDDLE LEVEL
LITERATURE

All Together

THEME
COMMUNITY

AUTHORS

Donna Alvermann
Linda Miller Cleary
Kenneth Donelson
Donald Gallo
Alice Haskins
J. Howard Johnston
John Lounsbury
Alleen Pace Nilsen
Robert Pavlik
Jewell Parker Rhodes
Alberto Alvaro Ríos
Sandra Schurr
Lyndon Searfoss
Julia Thomason
Max Thompson
Carl Zon

 D.C. Heath and Company
Lexington, Massachusetts / Toronto, Ontario

STAFF CREDITS

EDITORIAL Barbara A. Brennan, Helen Byers, Christopher Johnson, Kathleen Kennedy Kelley, Owen Shows, Rita M. Sullivan
Proofreading: JoAnne B. Sgroi

CONTRIBUTING WRITERS Nance Davidson, Florence Harris

SERIES DESIGN Robin Herr

BOOK DESIGN Caroline Bowden, Daniel Derdula, Susan Geer, Diana Maloney, Angela Sciaraffa, Bonnie Chayes Yousefian
Art Editing: Carolyn Langley

PHOTOGRAPHY *Series Photography Coordinator:* Carmen Johnson
Photo Research Supervisor: Martha Friedman
Photo Researchers: Wendy Enright, Linda Finigan, Po-yee McKenna, PhotoSearch, Inc., Gillian Speeth, Denise Theodores
Assignment Photography Coordinators: Susan Doheny, Gayna Hoffman, Shawna Johnston

COMPUTER PREPRESS Ricki Pappo, Kathy Meisl
Richard Curran, Michele Locatelli

PERMISSIONS Dorothy B. McLeod

PRODUCTION Patrick Connolly

Cover: © Superstock. **Cover Design:** Steve Snider

Published simultaneously in Canada

Printed in the United States of America

International Standard Book Number: 0-669-32098-6 (soft cover)
  3 4 5 6 7 8 9 10-RRD-99 98 97 96

International Standard Book Number: 0-669-38168-3 (hard cover)
  3 4 5 6 7 8 9 10-RRD-99 98 97 96 95

Middle Level Authors

Donna Alvermann, University of Georgia
Alice Haskins, Howard County Public Schools, Maryland
J. Howard Johnston, University of South Florida
John Lounsbury, Georgia College
Sandra Schurr, University of South Florida
Julia Thomason, Appalachian State University
Max Thompson, Appalachian State University
Carl Zon, California Assessment Collaborative

Literature and Language Arts Authors

Linda Miller Cleary, University of Minnesota
Kenneth Donelson, Arizona State University
Donald Gallo, Central Connecticut State University
Alleen Pace Nilsen, Arizona State University
Robert Pavlik, Cardinal Stritch College, Milwaukee
Jewell Parker Rhodes, Arizona State University
Alberto Alvaro Ríos, Arizona State University
Lyndon Searfoss, Arizona State University

Teacher Consultants

Suzanne Aubin, Patapsco Middle School, Ellicott City, Maryland
Judy Baxter, Newport News Public Schools, Newport News, Virginia
Saundra Bryn, Director of Research and Development, El Mirage, Arizona
Lorraine Gerhart, Elmbrook Middle School, Elm Grove, Wisconsin
Kathy Tuchman Glass, Burlingame Intermediate School, Burlingame, California
Lisa Mandelbaum, Crocker Middle School, Hillsborough, California
Lucretia Pannozzo, John Jay Middle School, Katonah, New York
Carol Schultz, Jerling Junior High, Orland Park, Illinois
Jeanne Siebenman, Grand Canyon University, Phoenix, Arizona
Gail Thompson, Garey High School, Pomona, California
Rufus Thompson, Grace Yokley School, Ontario, California
Tom Tufts, Conniston Middle School, West Palm Beach, Florida
Edna Turner, Harpers Choice Middle School, Columbia, Maryland
C. Anne Webb, Buerkle Junior High School, St. Louis, Missouri
Geri Yaccino, Thompson Junior High School, St. Charles, Illinois

CONTENTS

Launch Activity:
A PICTURE OF US   8-9

What does community mean to you?

ASKING BIG QUESTIONS ABOUT
THE THEME   10-11

What makes a community?

What communities do people belong to?

What responsibilities do people have to their community?

How do communities change?

THE LITERATURE

GARY SOTO   Seventh Grade   12-19

SHORT STORY

As the school community begins the fall semester, Victor becomes interested in a new subject.

CATHERINE CROCKER   'They think I'm an expert'   20-23
LATOYA HUNTER   from *The Diary of Latoya Hunter*   24-31

NONFICTION

Latoya describes her community to a new friend.

MICHAEL GRUNWALD   **Empowered to heal**   32-35

NONFICTION

Eight teenagers unite to save their community.

JOEL SCHWARTZ   **Break a Leg**   36-41

SHORT STORY

Elliot finds that following Dad's advice can be dangerous!

PHILLIP HOOSE   **Founders of the Children's Rain Forest**   42-53

NONFICTION

Children in Sweden help save the rain forests.

PHILLIP HOOSE   **Beni Seballos** **54-61**

NONFICTION

A girl finds a way of touching her grandmother's heart.

ISAAC ASIMOV   **The Fun They Had**   62-65

SHORT STORY

What will school be like in sixty years?

JERRY STANLEY   **Something to Watch and Our School from Children of the Dust Bowl**   66-77

NONFICTION

Children of a farm community build their own school.

NIKKI GIOVANNI   **Knoxville, Tennessee**   78-79

POEM

The speaker reflects on the summer joys of her neighborhood.

SANDRA CISNEROS   **Those Who Don't**   80-81

FICTION

How do some people feel about being in a different neighborhood?

MICKEY ROBERTS   **It's All in How You Say It**   82-85

NONFICTION

It's easy to misunderstand another culture.

IGNATIA BROKER   **The Forest Cries**   86-95

NONFICTION

Some thoughts on the history and experience of Native Americans.

JEWELL PARKER RHODES   **Block Party**   96-101

NONFICTION

A writer looks back on the neighborhood community of her childhood.

ASKING BIG QUESTIONS ABOUT THE LITERATURE

What makes a community? 102

What communities do people belong to? 103

What responsibilities do people have to their community? 104

How do communities change? 105

PROJECTS

1 WRITING WORKSHOP
A PROPOSAL FOR CHANGE 106-111
Does something need work in your community? Here's your chance to change the world!

2 COOPERATIVE LEARNING
A COMMUNITY OF THE FUTURE 112-113
What will communities of the future be like? Use your imagination to create a futuristic community on a planet of your choice!

3 HELPING YOUR COMMUNITY
DEVELOPING A PLAN OF ACTION 114-115
What does your community need? Create a plan of action to help your school, neighborhood, or town.

PUTTING IT ALL TOGETHER 116-117
What have you learned about the theme?

LITERARY ELEMENTS: Setting and Theme 118-119

GLOSSARY OF LITERARY TERMS 120-124

ACKNOWLEDGMENTS AND CREDITS 125

FULL PRONUNCIATION KEY FOR FOOTNOTED WORDS 126

A Picture of Us

The word *me* separates you from other people, but the word *us* links you to them. Using *us* means you see yourself not just as one person alone but as part of a *community*—a group of persons who have something in common or who share some daily experience, such as going to the same school or living in the same neighborhood.

What do you know about communities, and about the people and places that turn *me* into *us*? With a group of classmates, express what you know in a mural—a picture of *us*.

Think about your mural.

What does *community* mean to you? What groups of people do you feel part of? Think of how you could represent the idea of community in a mural. Could a community be represented by certain kinds of clothing, food, or a flag? Jot down your thoughts in your journal.

Make your mural.

Work with a group of five or six classmates to make a mural of a community you know, such as your school or neighborhood. Use poster paper or tape together sheets of notebook paper. Decide on a work plan before you start. Divide the mural into sections that you can work on individually, or come up with an overall design and work on it together.

Let's talk.

Discuss your mural. Use questions like these to guide your discussion:
- Why did we include the things we did?
- What do they mean to us?
- How are they linked to community?
- What do they tell us about communities?

Define community.

Think about the murals you've seen and then write your own definition of *community*. Let members of your group take turns reading their definitions. How do these definitions compare to yours? As your recorder takes notes, work toward a group definition. Keep revising until you come up with a definition that satisfies everyone. Finally write your definition on a piece of paper and attach it to the mural.

Asking Big Questions About the Theme

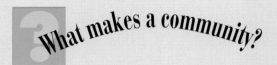

What makes a community?

Think about the communities that you belong to, such as your school or your neighborhood. Then, in your journal, complete these sentences with as many ideas as you can.

When I say *us*, I mean _____.

The things I associate with *us* are _____.

Now think of all the different kinds of communities in the world, from school communities like yours to the village communities in the rain forests of Costa Rica. Discuss what all these communities have in common. Decide what makes a community.

What communities do people belong to?

Your world is full of communities. Just look at your town, which is made up of many smaller communities. What are they? Work with one or more classmates. Draw a big circle and label it *TOWN*. Then take turns identifying the smaller communities within your town. To represent each of these communities, draw and label a small circle inside the big circle.

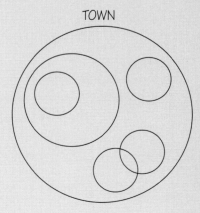

TOWN

What responsibilities do people have to their community?

What are your responsibilities to your school, neighborhood, and town? For example, have you ever volunteered to baby-sit while your neighbor voted? In your journal, draw the outline of your hand three times. Then label each outline with the name of one of these communities. In each finger, write a duty you have to that community. Compare your "hands" with those of your classmates.

How do communities change?

With a partner or small group, discuss changes in your school, neighborhood, and town over the years. Are your classes organized differently? Have stores opened or closed? Have bus routes changed? In your journal, make a chart to show the changes in one of your communities. Use the model below to help you.

Changes in My Neighborhood	
When I was 8	**Now**
Only grocery store, shoe store, pharmacy on Vine St.	Mini-mall

NOW

Think!

How do you feel about your communities? As you read *All Together*, think about how your communities compare with the communities in the stories and poems. Do the characters in the selections say what you might say about your community? Do they feel how you feel about belonging to a group?

SEVENTH GRADE

GARY SOTO

On the first day of school, Victor stood in line half an hour before he came to a wobbly card table. He was handed a packet of papers and a computer card on which he listed his one elective, French. He already spoke Spanish and English, but he thought some day he might travel to France, where it was cool; not like Fresno,[1] where summer days reached 110 degrees in the shade. There were rivers in France, and huge churches, and fair-skinned people everywhere, the way there were brown people all around Victor.

Besides, Teresa, a girl he had liked since they were in catechism[2] classes at Saint Theresa's, was taking French, too. With any luck they would be in the same class. Teresa is going to be my girl this year, he promised himself as he left the gym full of students in their new fall clothes. She was cute. And good at math, too, Victor thought as he walked down the hall to his homeroom. He ran into his friend, Michael Torres, by the water fountain that never turned off.

1. **Fresno** [frez′ nō]: city in central California.
2. **catechism** [kat′ ə kiz əm]: a book of questions and answers about religion.

They shook hands, *raza*-style,[3] and jerked their heads at one another in a *saludo de vato*.[4] "How come you're making a face?" asked Victor.

"I ain't making a face, *ese*.[5] This *is* my face." Michael said his face had changed during the summer. He had read a *GQ* magazine that his older brother borrowed from the Book Mobile and noticed that the male models all had the same look on their faces. They would stand, one arm around a beautiful woman, and *scowl*. They would sit at a pool, their rippled stomachs dark with shadow, and *scowl*. They would sit at dinner tables, cool drinks in their hands, and *scowl*.

"I think it works," Michael said. He scowled and let his upper lip quiver. His teeth showed along with the ferocity of his soul. "Belinda Reyes walked by a while ago and looked at me," he said.

Victor didn't say anything, though he thought his friend looked pretty strange. They talked about recent movies, baseball, their parents, and the horrors of picking grapes in order to buy their fall clothes. Picking grapes was like living in Siberia, except hot and more boring.

"What classes are you taking?" Michael said, scowling.

"French. How 'bout you?"

"Spanish. I ain't so good at it, even if I'm Mexican."

"I'm not either, but I'm better at it than math, that's for sure."

A tinny, three-beat bell propelled students to their homerooms. The two friends socked each other in the arm and went their ways, Victor thinking, man, that's weird. Michael thinks making a face makes him handsome.

On his way to his homeroom, Victor tried a scowl. He felt foolish, until out of the corner of his eye he saw a girl looking at

---

3. ***raza*-style** [rä´ sä]: Spanish slang, here meaning in a special style known by friends.

4. ***saludo de vato*** [sä lü´ dō dā vä´ tō]: Spanish slang, meaning a greeting between "cool" guys.

5. ***ese*** [ā´ sā]: Spanish slang, here meaning "dude" or "you."

him. Umm, he thought, maybe it does work. He scowled with greater conviction.

In homeroom, roll was taken, emergency cards were passed out, and they were given a bulletin to take home to their parents. The principal, Mr. Belton, spoke over a crackling loudspeaker, welcoming the students to a new year, new experiences, and new friendships. The students squirmed in their chairs and ignored him. They were anxious to go to first period. Victor sat calmly, thinking of Teresa, who sat two rows away, reading a paperback novel. This would be his lucky year. She was in his homeroom, and would probably be in his English and math classes. And, of course, French.

The bell rang for first period, and the students herded noisily through the door. Only Teresa lingered, talking with the homeroom teacher.

"So you think I should talk to Mrs. Gaines?" she asked the teacher. "She would know about ballet?"

"She would be a good bet," the teacher said. Then added, "Or the gym teacher, Mrs. Garza."

Victor lingered, keeping his head down and staring at his desk. He wanted to leave when she did so he could bump into her and say something clever.

He watched her on the sly. As she turned to leave, he stood up and hurried to the door, where he managed to catch her eye. She smiled and said, "Hi, Victor."

He smiled back and said, "Yeah, that's me." His brown face blushed. Why hadn't he said, "Hi, Teresa," or "How was your summer?" or something nice?

As Teresa walked down the hall, Victor walked the other way, looking back, admiring how gracefully she walked, one foot in front of the other. So much for being in the same class, he thought. As he trudged to English, he practiced scowling.

In English they reviewed the parts of speech. Mr. Lucas, a portly man, waddled down the aisle, asking, "What is a noun?"

"A person, place, or thing," said the class in unison.

"Yes, now somebody give me an example of a person—you, Victor Rodriguez."

"Teresa," Victor said automatically. Some of the girls giggled. They knew he had a crush on Teresa. He felt himself blushing again.

"Correct," Mr. Lucas said. "Now provide me with a place."

Mr. Lucas called on a freckled kid who answered, "Teresa's house with a kitchen full of big brothers."

After English, Victor had math, his weakest subject. He sat in the back by the window, hoping that he would not be called on. Victor understood most of the problems, but some of the stuff looked like the teacher made it up as she went along. It was confusing, like the inside of a watch.

After math he had a fifteen-minute break, then social studies, and, finally, lunch. He bought a tuna casserole with buttered rolls, some fruit cocktail, and milk. He sat with Michael, who practiced scowling between bites.

Girls walked by and looked at him.

"See what I mean, Vic?" Michael scowled. "They love it."

"Yeah, I guess so."

They ate slowly, Victor scanning the horizon for a glimpse of Teresa. He didn't see her. She must have brought lunch, he thought, and is eating outside. Victor scraped his plate and left Michael, who was busy scowling at a girl two tables away.

The small, triangle-shaped campus bustled with students talking about their new classes. Everyone was in a sunny mood. Victor hurried to the bag lunch area, where he sat down and opened his math book. He moved his lips as if he were reading, but his mind was somewhere else. He raised his eyes slowly and looked around. No Teresa.

He lowered his eyes, pretending to study, then looked slowly to the left. No Teresa. He turned a page in the book and stared at some math problems that scared him because he knew he would have to do them eventually. He looked to the right. Still no sign of her. He stretched out lazily in an attempt to disguise his snooping.

Then he saw her. She was sitting with a girlfriend under a plum tree. Victor moved to a table near her and daydreamed about taking her to a movie. When the bell sounded, Teresa looked up, and their eyes met. She smiled sweetly and gathered her books. Her next class was French, same as Victor's.

They were among the last students to arrive in class, so all the good desks in the back had already been taken. Victor was forced to sit near the front, a few desks away from Teresa, while Mr. Bueller wrote French words on the chalkboard. The bell rang, and Mr. Bueller wiped his hands, turned to the class, and said, *"Bonjour."* [6]

"Bonjour," braved a few students.

"Bonjour," Victor whispered. He wondered if Teresa heard him.

Mr. Bueller said that if the students studied hard, at the end of the year they could go to France and be understood by the populace.

One kid raised his hand and asked, "What's 'populace'?"

"The people, the people of France."

Mr. Bueller asked if anyone knew French. Victor raised his hand, wanting to impress Teresa. The teacher beamed and said, *"Très bien. Parlez-vous français?"* [7]

Victor didn't know what to say. The teacher wet his lips and asked something else in French. The room grew silent. Victor felt all eyes staring at him. He tried to bluff his way out by making noises that sounded French.

"La me vava me con le grandma," [8] he said uncertainly.

Mr. Bueller, wrinkling his face in curiosity, asked him to speak up.

Great rosebushes of red bloomed on Victor's cheeks. A river of nervous sweat ran down his palms. He felt awful. Teresa sat a few desks away, no doubt thinking he was a fool. Without looking at Mr. Bueller, Victor mumbled, "Frenchie oh wewe gee in September." [9]

Mr. Bueller asked Victor to repeat what he had said.

---

6. **bonjour** [bôN zhür′]: French for "hello."
7. **Très bien. Parlez-vous français?** [tre byen pär lā′ vù frän se′]: French for "Very good. Do you speak French?"
8. **La me vava me con le grandma** [lä mā vä′ vä mā côn lā grän′ mä]: Victor is pretending to speak French.
9. **Frenchie oh wewe gee in September:** Victor is talking nonsense.

"Frenchie oh wewe gee in September," Victor repeated.

Mr. Bueller understood that the boy didn't know French and turned away. He walked to the blackboard and pointed to the words on the board with his steel-edged ruler.

"*Le bateau*,"[10] he sang.

"*Le bateau*," the students repeated.

"*Le bateau est sur l'eau*,"[11] he sang.

"*Le bateau est sur l'eau*."

Victor was too weak from failure to join the class. He stared at the board and wished he had taken Spanish, not French. Better yet, he wished he could start his life over. He had never been so embarrassed. He bit his thumb until he tore off a sliver of skin.

The bell sounded for fifth period, and Victor shot out of the room, avoiding the stares of the other kids, but had to return for his math book. He looked sheepishly at the teacher, who was erasing the board, then widened his eyes in terror at Teresa who stood in front of him. "I didn't know you knew French," she said. "That was good."

Mr. Bueller looked at Victor, and Victor looked back. Oh please, don't say anything, Victor pleaded with his eyes. I'll wash your car, mow your lawn, walk your dog—anything! I'll be your best student, and I'll clean your erasers after school.

10. *le bateau* [lə bä tō′]: French for "boat."
11. *le bateau est sur l'eau* [lə bä tō′ ā syr lō]: French for "The boat is on the water."

Mr. Bueller shuffled through the papers on his desk. He smiled and hummed as he sat down to work. He remembered his college years when he dated a girlfriend in borrowed cars. She thought he was rich because each time he picked her up he had a different car. It was fun until he had spent all his money on her and had to write home to his parents because he was broke.

Victor couldn't stand to look at Teresa. He was sweaty with shame. "Yeah, well, I picked up a few things from movies and books, and stuff like that." They left the class together. Teresa asked him if he would help her with her French.

"Sure, anytime," Victor said.

"I won't be bothering you, will I?"

"Oh no, I like being bothered."

"*Bonjour,*" Teresa said, leaving him outside her next class. She smiled and pushed wisps of hair from her face.

"Yeah, right, *bonjour,*" Victor said. He turned and headed to his class. The rosebushes of shame on his face became bouquets of love. Teresa is a great girl, he thought. And Mr. Bueller is a good guy.

He raced to metal shop. After metal shop there was biology, and after biology a long sprint to the public library, where he checked out three French textbooks.

He was going to like seventh grade.

GARY SOTO

Gary Soto was born in 1952 in Fresno, California, and grew up in a poor Mexican American family. Like the boys in "Seventh Grade," Soto earned money as a farm worker. Later he began to write poetry about his childhood memories and published his first book of poems in 1977. Soto has gone on to write fiction—much of it for young adults—while teaching Chicano Studies and English at the University of California in Berkeley.

Most of Soto's short stories are based on his experiences while growing up. "Seventh Grade" is one of the stories in *Baseball in April*. You can find more of Soto's stories in his book *Local News*.

'They think I'm an expert'

Girl's diary spurs letters by peers, notice of Hollywood

By Catherine Crocker
Associated Press

Latoya Hunter

NEW YORK—Latoya Hunter is just 14 years old, but recently, the mail brought a packet of letters from teen-agers in Brooklyn, many of them girls seeking advice about boys and their parents.

"As I was reading it, I couldn't believe it," said Latoya, whose face still has the softness of childhood.

"I mean, I'm going through those problems now, and they think I am an expert."

They think she is an expert because they know her deepest thoughts, expressed in a diary she kept during her first year in junior high school.

The Diary of Latoya Hunter, published earlier this year, is about the stuff of young girls' lives—school, friendships, boys, television, the urge for independence and conflicts with her mother.

But the slim volume, which runs 131 pages, goes deeper. It is also about being a black, immigrant girl growing up in the Bronx.

Latoya wrote in her diary about the gray, treeless streets of her neighborhood, the deadly violence around her, teen-age pregnancy, the poverty of caring and learning at her school and her homesickness for Jamaica.[1]

1. **Jamaica** [jə mā′ kə]: island country in the West Indies, south of Cuba.

It's the ordinariness of her preadolescent world against this troubled background that draws the reader into her diary. Latoya rhapsodizes[2] about her passion for junk food and TV, and then, in painfully clear prose, writes about the gunshots that killed a store clerk who sold her candy.

"Today gunshots echo in my head," Latoya wrote on Jan. 9, 1991.

"They are the same gunshots that killed an innocent human being right across from my house last night. They are the same gunshots that have scarred me, I think, forever."

'It was mostly luck'

Latoya's world has expanded beyond its old Bronx borders because of a devoted teacher, a chance newspaper article and her gift for writing.

"I think it was mostly luck," Latoya said.

But then she added, "I think, like, I am a good spokesperson for people around my age, for kids who feel that they don't count in anything, that they're being held back from being who they really want to be by outside things, like parents and friends and the kind of environment you live in."

A 1990 newspaper article about the graduation of Latoya's sixth-grade class said her English teacher wrote, "The world is waiting for Latoya!" on her report card. An editor at a publishing company saw the story and was inspired.

He contacted the teacher to ask whether Latoya would be interested in keeping a diary her first year in junior high. Latoya was offered a $3,000 advance and will receive $25,000 for the paperback rights.

Her first entries began "Dear Diary," then she decided to personalize her journal because "you've become like a best friend to me." She named it Janice Page, after her best friend in Jamaica.

"I like guys," Latoya wrote. "There, I said it. It's easy to say to you, but my mother would give me a real hard time if she heard me say that. She believes a normal 12-year-old should only obey her parents, go to school, learn her lessons, and come home

---

2. **rhapsodizes** [rap′ sə dīz əz]: talks or writes in an overly enthusiastic way.

everyday and listen to her parents some more."

She recounts her first relationship with a boy (they didn't go out, they just opened their hearts over the telephone), her brother's wedding (she was a bridesmaid in blue), the birth of her unmarried sister's boy, and a much-anticipated trip to Jamaica that left her deeply disappointed.

Her conclusion: "With understanding, I think I will achieve anything I want."

'Colors I see are . . . dull'

On a cold and windy afternoon, Latoya, dressed in jeans and gold hoop earrings, was back in her old Bronx neighborhood, giving a reporter a tour. She harbors no nostalgia[3] for it.

"It really makes you feel down to walk around and see the things around you," she wrote. "The only colors I see are brown and gray— dull colors. Maybe there are others, but the dull ones are the ones I see. Maybe if the streets were cleaner, and I would see colors like red and yellow, my surroundings would be more appealing."

Until she was 8, Latoya was raised by relatives in Jamaica while her parents were in the New York area struggling to make a new life for themselves. Latoya's old house, where she lived with her family on the second floor, has a chain-link fence in front and flowers in the planters that, she said, make it look better than it did when she lived there.

"It was the ugliest house on the whole block," she said. "And I never liked to bring anybody over."

Relatives live in the ground-floor apartment. Eager to see a newborn cousin, Latoya drops by for a visit. A stale smell fills the dark, sparsely[4] furnished rooms. The walls are stained and cracked.

Today, her mother, Linneth, works evenings as a nurse's aide; her father, Linton, works overnight as a security guard. And Latoya now lives in a well-kept apartment in a blue house on a tree-lined street in Mount Vernon, N.Y., a city just north of the Bronx.

---

3. **nostalgia** [no stal′ jə]: a painful loneliness that results from thinking about one's home, country, city, and so forth.
4. **sparsely** [spärs′ lē]: thinly; very little spread out.

Overwhelming response

The book's sales started out slowly, but the media response has been overwhelming. Latoya has been interviewed by reporters, appeared on television talk shows and news programs—including one that airs in Japan—and met the Jamaican prime minister.

Two movie companies are bidding for the rights to the book, said Richard Marek, her editor at Crown Publishing Inc.

But Latoya says wistfully[5] that her parents have never talked to her directly about the diary's contents, although she believes both have read it.

"If I do an interview or something," she said, "they say 'I'm proud of you' and stuff, but they never really said that to me about the book, like, you know, 'You did a good job and I'm proud of you.'"

She's a sophomore in high school, having skipped a grade. Ithaca College and Columbia University already have approached her, she said.

She wants to study psychology[6]

and be a writer. She also says that after she has had a job for a year, she wants to have a baby.

Sitting at her dining-room table, she fidgets with a pendant necklace belonging to her mother. She is shy, soft-spoken, but articulate.

"It's like everybody's dream to be in America," Latoya said. "And now that I am here, I just don't want to waste the opportunities I have."

But as doors open to worlds she never dreamed existed, there is a loss of innocence to which she is still adjusting. In her diary, she wrote, "I've never come across discrimination against me for being black."

Now she has.

A few weeks ago, when she went to the Manhattan office of a national women's magazine to be interviewed about her book, the woman at the front desk asked "if I was there to deliver anything."

"She could have said, like, 'Could I help you?' or something," Latoya said. "I guess they didn't expect someone like me to be there."

---

5. **wistfully** [wist′ fəl ē]: longingly, yearningly.
6. **psychology** [sī kol′ ə jē]: study of the mind.

From *The Diary of Latoya Hunter*

LATOYA HUNTER

Mural painted by children from the nearby community, 1989, Col. Young Park, New York City

September 17, 1990

Dear Diary,

I have good news. On Thursday and Friday there'll be no school. It's the Jewish New Year. It doesn't count for me because I'm not Jewish. I really respect these people though. Last year in school I learned about Adolph Hitler[1] and all the terrible things he did to them. He was a psycho if you ask me. I can't understand why people

1. **Adolph Hitler** [ā′ dolf hit′ lər]: Nazi dictator of Germany from 1933 to 1945.

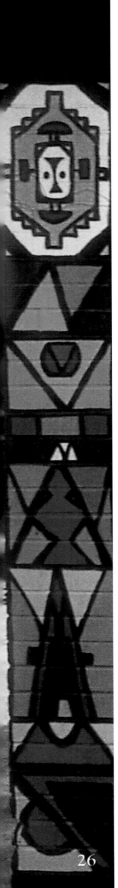

discriminate against others for simple things like skin color and religion. I strongly believe this world should be non-racist. I've never come across discrimination against me for being black. I know racism is going on in all parts of the world but the fight is still going on too. That is something to be thankful for. Things like Mandela[2] recently being freed has kept my hope alive.

September 18, 1990

Dear Diary,

Today felt like a sneak preview of winter and a sad end to summer. It was fun while it lasted. I spent most of August in Toronto.[3] It's such a beautiful city. It's clean and peaceful. In other words, not my style. I like action. It's not so much the place that appeals to me, it's my relatives living there. That includes my grandparents on my mom's side, my aunt Chunnie, and four of my cousins. The oldest is 20 and the youngest is now 16. That's the only girl, Ann. We grew up like sisters! Like me their mom lived apart from them (in Canada), then took them up. Then she took up my grandparents. My cousins are who I grew up with excluding my Aunt Chunnie and her youngest son, and they were the only people I knew how to love until I was eight. That's when I left Jamaica, my homeland, the place where my life was crafted. Sadly, until that time, my life was crafted without my parents. They were here in N.Y., struggling to make enough money to get my sister, two brothers and me to share with them the American dream. I didn't know my father until he met us at the airport. He left when I was a baby. I've really gotten to know him over the past four years though. When I first saw him at the airport, I thought "Well this is the famous Daddy!" Everyone, even my cousins call him Daddy. Our families were that close. I can't forget he was in a hurry to get home to watch a big baseball game on t.v. After

2. **Mandela** [man del′ ə]: Nelson, black South African lawyer and leader of the African National Congress, who fought for civil rights and was imprisoned by the South African government from 1964 to 1990.
3. **Toronto** [tə ron′ tō]: city in southeast Canada, capital of the province of Ontario.

that was over, he pretty much put all his attention into us. I can remember once when I was sick, and I'll never forget this, he made me soup and made me stay in bed. I was like, "Wow! This is like t.v." I guess in Jamaica I never pictured a father making soup for his kid. I pictured the mother doing those things, never the man. He isn't easily upset or worked up. He hardly yells at me. That works with me because if I do something wrong and someone yells at me, I don't feel guilty about what I've done, just angry at the person yelling. He just goes with the flow. He was really easy to get used to.

My mother is really complex though. I still don't understand her. I had a faint memory of her while I was in Jamaica. She had left when I was 3 or 4. Anyways, they succeeded in getting my brothers, sister and myself up here. When we first got here she worked as a live-in housekeeper in Poughkeepsie[4] for some very rich people. She only came home on Friday and left again on Sunday. We hardly ever saw her but she called all the time. What got her to quit was when I first started going to P.S. 94. I was in computer class for the first time and when I saw that everyone knew what to do, I got depressed. I never saw one before in my life. I cried and cried and the teacher sent me home because I said I had a stomach ache.

Anyway, my mom heard about it and decided she didn't want to be away when things like that happened. I finally had her full-time. We enjoyed ourselves at first, being together all the time. But the excitement wore off and when I was around ten, we began the phase we're in now.

As I said, I'm living in the Bronx,[5] a place where walking alone at night is a major risk. The streets are so dirty and there's graffiti everywhere. It really makes you feel down to walk around and see the things around you. The only colors I see are brown and grey—dull colors. Maybe there are others but the dull ones are the ones I see. Maybe if the streets were cleaner, and I would see colors like red and yellow, my surroundings would be more appealing but for now, all I see is dullness and cloudiness. There aren't any pleasant smells

4. **Poughkeepsie** [pə kip′ sē]: city in southeastern New York, on the Hudson River.
5. **Bronx** [brongks]: section of New York City.

coming from anywhere as I walk the neighborhood—just the smell of nothingness. There are a few stores very close to where I live. They are one of the few things that are familiar to me in this neighborhood. Everyone knows me in these stores because if nothing else, I'm a junk food fanatic! There's one at the corner, one around the corner and one in between. Besides them, everything is grey.

Am I lucky or what? I would say not but it wouldn't be true entirely. There are so many opportunities we've gotten that we wouldn't dream of getting in Jamaica. I guess that's why they call this the land of opportunity. My mom works in a hospital not far from our house. She's a nurses assistant, my father does security work. It isn't a big income family but I'll make it. I think we all will.

September 19, 1990

Dear Diary,

Just knowing I don't have to go to school tomorrow made my entire day today. I stayed outside with my friends after school. I haven't done that for such a long time. I almost forgot how much fun I had with them.

I'll tell you about Deborah first, she's a distant cousin. She's the one who showed me around at first and introduced me to people. She's like the leader of our crew. She can act pushy sometimes but I like her. We would call her a Don Girl in Jamaican. That means she's someone you just respect.

Then there's Denise and Monique, they're sisters, but they don't really get along. Denise changes her personality a lot and frankly I can't keep up with her. Monique however, stays the same. She's funny and just a fun-loving person. There's also Lisa and Isabelle. Lisa's cool, Isabelle's someone I can't explain. I'm not really crazy about her.

They, especially Deborah, have taught me a lot. Over the years they've shown me how to come out of my shell and have fun. They were the ones who introduced me to things like parties, music, boys . . . some crazy things we've done! One time we planned to go visit a cemetery at night. Is that crazy or what? Only we would do something like that!

September 20, 1990

Dear Diary,

I spent the day helping out my friend Anika. She's moving out of her apartment. I'll still get to see her though, she's still going to go to my school.

We met an old lady on the street. We walked with her to the bus stop. I think in that short time we spent walking, she actually told us her life story. She told us she's going back to high school and she seemed to be proud of herself. She told us about God and that He had been her best friend ever since she was our age. It was really interesting to listen to someone who has lived and experienced so much. At first, I was just trying not to be rude so I listened, but soon I found myself wanting to hear what she had to say. I realize now that everyone has a life to them. I see so many faces everyday, it was nice to go beyond the face for once.

September 21, 1990

Dear Diary,

Today three of my relatives from Canada came for a visit; my grandfather and two boy cousins Glendon and Dexton. They'll be here until Sunday. I hope God keeps them safe for the few days they'll be here. The other day a guy from Utah was stabbed to death while protecting his family on the train. That is a sad example of the crime in New York especially since he was just visiting for the weekend. The crime is really getting ridiculous here.

If I had a choice now, I would choose to leave this place. I just can't feel safe here. I have good reasons too. My father was almost shot when he used to drive a cab at nights. My brother also came close to being a victim of crime. He was held up at gunpoint at the movie theater where he works in Manhattan. Fortunately he wasn't hurt. I'm really scared to be here.

My friend Lisa wasn't as lucky with brothers as I was. Her brother was shot 12 times just the other day. I heard he was on the way to the

store and someone waited for him and did the job. It was probably drug-related. He looked like someone involved in those things, sorry to say. She's still mourning his death. Anyways Diary, that's the way things are in New York city, my home.

September 23, 1990

Dear Diary,

The weekend was great as always. On Saturday I went to see my aunt Rita. She lives 15 minutes away in the Bronx. Everyone went: my parents, sister, and my relatives visiting from Canada. It was a nice evening. Afterwards I went to my friend's sister's baby shower. I couldn't stay long though because I wasn't supposed to be there in the first place. My mother disapproves of me being at that house. I don't know what she thinks goes on up there but I know she's wrong. She wrong about everything. She thinks there are things going on that she doesn't know about, but there aren't. I think in her mind she sees Deborah and everyone else with a bunch of guys partying and making out—what else could she think? I think she knows I wouldn't do anything like drugs. If only she'd understand, then I wouldn't feel guilty every time I want to be with my friends.

Today, Sunday, I went to church. My relatives left and went back home. It was nice having them here, even for a short time. I get to take communion⁶ now. Personally I don't like the bread but it's supposed to be the body of Christ so I eat it. I always make sure however that I have candy to get the taste out of my mouth. Well Diary, the vacation is over. I have to face school tomorrow. I don't mind though, I'm going to try to feel comfortable there—I'll really like my classes and make more friends. I think things would really look up then. So far I like Home and Careers. I'm not so crazy about the teacher but I like the idea of planning and thinking about later on in life.

6. **communion** [kə myü′ nyən]: the act of receiving bread as a part of some Christian religious services.

September 25, 1990

Dear Diary,

Why does school have to come with music teachers?! You would not believe what mine is going to make the class do. I'm talking major embarrassing! The whole class has to sing "We Are the World" in front of the whole school! Can you believe it? I mean, the song is so old. It's not fair! I bet the kids will boo us off the stage, they're good at that if anything. We're supposed to do this thing on Wednesday. Talk about short notice! We rehearsed and I must say, sound terrible. The boys are off key and it's just a mess. I hope we get it together before Wednesday, we can't afford to give the older kids more reason not to like us.

September 30, 1990

Dear Diary,

I think I need a name for you. You've become like a best friend to me, you're someone I can talk to without being argued with. I think I know just the name for you. I'll call you Janice after my best friend from Jamaica. We were like sisters before I left. Over the years we've grown apart though, the letters have stopped but that friendship is still going on within me!

So today I christen[7] you diary, Janice Page.

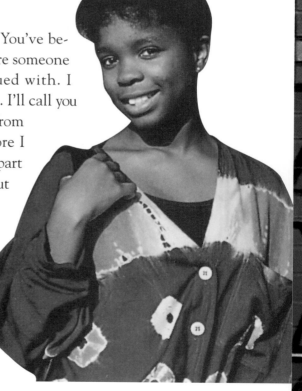

7. **christen** [kris′n]: to give a name to someone or something, as in baptism.

from *The Boston Globe*   April 22, 1993

Empowered

Clinton to honor Brockton

By Michael Grunwald

GLOBE STAFF

BROCKTON[1]—There was a war raging on the streets of this troubled city, a violent clash of well-armed teen-agers who neither feared death nor shrunk from causing it. And there was a new group declaring war on that war: Our Positive Posse,[2] eight teen-agers determined to educate their peers about the dangers of gangs and drugs.

So there was a meeting, held in the Crescent Court housing project,[3] on Nov. 2, 1991. The Posse's peer leaders spoke about peace, about taking back Brockton, about setting a positive example. Forty teen-agers pledged their support for the Posse.

This afternoon, President Clinton will recognize the Posse's work by awarding it the President's Volunteer Action Award in a Rose Garden ceremony.

The Posse is one of 20 groups selected for the honor out of more than 4,300 nominees, stirring up an outpouring of pride in a city that

---

1. **Brockton** [brok′ tən]: city in southeastern Massachusetts.
2. **posse** [pos′ ē]: group working together.
3. **housing project** [proj′ ekt]: group of apartment houses run as a unit, especially as a part of public housing.

to heal

antiviolence group

has grown accustomed to numbing headlines about its chronic[4] woes: not enough water, too much political infighting, not enough money, too much crime.

Things weren't always so bright. At that 1991 meeting was a rising young singer named Christopher Bender. The next day, Bender was gunned down in a car parked outside his mother's Crescent Court home. And for a fleeting time, the Posse's leaders wondered if there was any use even trying to save their crumbling community.

4. **chronic** [kron´ ik]: lasting a long time.

"Yeah, when Chris got killed, we were really down," said Ollie Spears Jr., 18. "I figured the program would probably fall through the cracks. But we had a powerful, positive message to deliver."

"You hear all these horrible things about Brockton," said Police Chief Paul Studenski. "Well, these kids are making a real difference."

Members of the Posse swung into action soon after Bender was killed, organizing a Holiday Peace Bazaar to help heal their traumatized neighborhood. The group has led peace marches, peace forums and dozens of peace workshops for Brockton youngsters. It has branched out from the Crescent Court and Hillside Village development—where requests for police assistance have decreased more than 90 percent since the group began its grass-roots work—to the entire city.

The concept behind the Posse is as revolutionary as it is simple: Instead of telling kids what to do, let kids tell kids what to do. It is a concept at the heart of Teen Empowerment Inc., a private company hired by the Brockton Housing Authority to get the Posse off the ground.

"People always talk about empowerment, but they're usually just talking," said Tina Freimuth, 31, project coordinator for the Posse. "You've really got to believe in the power of youth. Kids won't always listen to adults, but they listen to each other."

Teen Empowerment administers similar teen-run programs in Lowell, Lawrence, New Bedford and Boston, as well as a citywide initiative[5] in Louisville, Ky. Director Stanley Pollack says programs run by teen-agers for teen-agers could offer Clinton an inexpensive, effective and easily replicated[6] strategy for reinvigorating[7] the nation's urban centers.

"This isn't a cure-all, but it will save a lot of lives," said Pollack, who said the Brockton program cost only $70,000 last year. "You could start this all across the country, no problem whatsoever, and

5. **initiative** [i nish ē ə tiv]: the first step in starting a task.
6. **replicated** [rep′ lə kat əd]: exactly reproduced, copied.
7. **reinvigorating** [rē in vig′ ə rāt ing]: filling again with life and energy.

you'd save millions of dollars in the long run."

It's hard to put a dollar value on crimes that never happen, on potential criminals whose lives are turned around, and potential victims who win unseen reprieves. Spears says that if he hadn't gotten involved in the Posse, he probably would be in jail today. Marcia Fernandes, 17, can only wonder if the Posse could have saved her brother Wayne, who was shot in the back and killed at a Brockton party in 1984.

"Adults haven't been able to solve young people's problems," Fernandes said. "We've got to solve them ourselves."

Yesterday, the Posse was dined (but not wined—peer leaders' contracts prohibit them from touching alcohol) by a horde of smiling politicians. Today, they will be honored by the president. Tomorrow, the group will be back on the streets of Brockton, and its battle will continue. Gangs, drugs and violence still tear at the fabric of this struggling city, still pose a constant threat to Brockton's youth.

"People are beginning to see that we can make a change, but everything isn't roses yet," Spears said. "We've still got a war to fight."

Break a Leg

JOEL SCHWARTZ

I wouldn't have gone to the "Getting to Know You" dance at school if it hadn't been for my father. He wouldn't have talked to me about it if it hadn't been for my mother. She wouldn't have talked to him about it if it hadn't been for my best friend Myron's mother. My best friend's mother wouldn't have talked to my mother about it if it hadn't been for my best friend. Myron wouldn't have talked to his mother about it if I hadn't talked to him about it, so I guess I'm to blame for everything.

It's not that I don't like dances and it's certainly not that I don't like girls. It's just that, well, all the twelve-year-old girls in the world are much taller than all the twelve-year-old boys. I wouldn't mind having to look at them straight in the eye, but having to look up all the time is embarrassing and it hurts my neck too. When you dance with a girl, they are supposed to be able to put their head on your shoulder, not their chin on your head.

So when Myron asked me at lunch, "Are you going to the 'Getting to Know You' dance?" I said, "Are you kidding? Nobody's going to that dance."

Myron took a giant bite of his sandwich and said, "Emrymoday ish gowig."

"Every Monday, what did you say?" I asked.

Myron wiped a large glob of mustard off his chin with his sleeve. "I said, everybody I know is going." Myron looked at the glob of mustard that now decorated his sleeve and without hesitation ground it into his pants. "Everybody, that is, except you."

I stared down at the spot on Myron's pants and then up at a new glob on his chin. At this rate, by the end of lunch, he would be wearing palomino-colored[1] pants and a white shirt with gold cuffs. "Name one person who's going."

"Me!"

"Besides you."

"Todd Murray."

"Mr. Murray, our math teacher?" Myron nodded. "He has to go. He's the chaperon. Besides, teachers don't count."

"Come on, go." I shook my head no. "For me?" I shook my head no again. "Why not?" This time the mustard had migrated up both cheeks.

"Why do you use so much mustard on your sandwich?" I asked, purposely changing the subject.

"Because I hate the taste of the meat," replied Myron.

"If you hate the taste of the meat so much, why don't you put a different kind of meat on your sandwich?"

"If I put on the meat that I liked, I wouldn't put on any mustard, and I like mustard on my sandwich." I stood up to go. "Not so fast. Why won't you go to the dance? Are you too chicken to go?"

"I don't want to talk about it anymore," I replied. "Finish eating your mustard sandwich and have a good time at the dance. You can tell me about it on Monday."

I thought I had heard the last of it, but after dinner that night my father asked me to go into the den because he wanted to talk to me about something. This usually means I've done something wrong and my mother has delegated my father to handle it.

"I've cleaned up my room," I said. "I did all my homework. I'll read a book for half an hour before I go to sleep, and I took out the trash."

My father smiled. "Why aren't you going to the 'Getting to Know You' dance?"

"How do you know that?" I asked.

"Your mother was talking to Myron's mother and—"

1. **palomino-colored** [pal´ ə me´ nō]: the cream color of a palomino horse.

"I don't want to go, that's all. What's the big deal?"

My father lit his pipe and leaned back in his chair. This usually meant he was going to tell a story about himself when he was my age. "When I was your age and just starting seventh grade like you, my school had a 'Getting to Know You' dance too, and I didn't want to go either. My dad sat me down, just like this, and said to me, 'I'll bet you're a little afraid to go to the dance.' 'Afraid?' I replied. 'I'm not afraid of any school dance.' 'Not of the dance,' he continued, 'but of the girls. Girls can be scary at your age. They act like they feel more comfortable in social situations than boys, but they're just as scared as you are. Go to the dance, act like you know what you're doing, and I'll bet you'll have a good time.' I didn't want to admit it then, but what your grandfather said to me that day made sense and I decided to go to the dance. The night of the dance my father drove me to the school and as I got out of the car he said 'Break a leg.' That's an expression actors use when they want to wish another actor good luck on the night of a performance. I think he did that purposely because he knew I'd have to be a good actor that night to hide my nervousness. I was nervous that night, but I covered it well and I ended up having a great time. Think about it."

I sat by myself in the den for a long time after Dad left and thought about what he just said. Usually what Dad says is either dumb or old-fashioned. This time he surprised me with something right on. Was he getting smarter?

After I called Myron and told him I had decided to go to the dance I spent half of the next twenty-four hours in and out of the bathroom. It was certainly a local record and probably a national and international one too. I could see myself in the Guinness Book of World Records for Most Trips in One Day to the Bathroom Without Actually Doing Anything.

I hardly ate dinner. After showering I smoothed on a manly hair gel, splashed on a mentholly after-shave, and sprayed on a musky deodorant. I smelled muskmantholly magnificent. I almost got out of the house with my old sneakers, but my mom made me go back and put on my new slippery loafers.

My father drove Myron and me to the dance. "Break a leg," he yelled as I got out of the car.

"What's that all about?" asked Myron.

"Who knows," I replied. "Probably some weird expression he picked up when he was my age."

When we got to the gym steps, I scuffed the bottom of my new shoes to take away some of the slipperiness. The gym was decorated with blue and white streamers and red, white, and yellow balloons. At one end was a large sign picturing a boy and girl dancing. It said WELCOME, SEVENTH GRADERS. Tables with punch, cookies, pretzels, and potato chips lined both side walls. The bleachers were filled with boys and the dance floor was filled with girls.

Myron and I walked to the top of the bleachers and sat down. I would have been very happy sitting there all evening, but the teacher chaperons had a different agenda. Without any warning they went into the stands and shooed all the boys out onto the floor. *Time to start acting*, I told myself.

Mr. Murray grabbed the microphone and said, "Girls make a circle." When they finished he said, "Boys make a circle around the girls' circle."

"Just what I wanted to do," I said to Myron. "Hold your hand and go around and around in a circle."

"When the music starts," instructed Mr. Murray, "I want the girls to circle clockwise and the boys to circle counterclockwise." The music started, and around both circles went. "When the music stops I want you to take the person in front of you for a partner."

Things were beginning to get serious. My heart was beating double time to the music and my muskmantholly mist was turning to must.[2] I secretly prayed for the song never to end. My prayer went unanswered and I found myself face to face with a girl—a tall girl—a very tall, muscular girl.

Act calm, I told myself. So what if her grandfather was Paul Bunyan. I smiled, she smiled back. I didn't know what to do next, so I smiled again.

2. **must** [must]: mold.

"Introduce yourself to your partner," said Mr. Murray.

"I'm Elliot."

"I'm Paula."

Paula Bunyan, I thought. Should I ask if she has a pet ox at home? *Be calm, Elliot. Be Calm.*

"To get things warmed up," said Mr. Murray, "I thought we might start off with a Mexican hat dance. Cross your hands and take hold of your partner." My palms were soaking wet and I wiped them on my pants before I grabbed Paula's hands. "Left foot, right foot, left-right-left. Do that combination two times. Go." Even though I could tell everyone around me thought this was dumb, we all did it. I could tell my shoes were still a little slippery. "Now, with your hands still crossed, swing your partner around. Go." *Next thing he'll want us to do is a whole dance of this*, I thought. "Now I want you to put both steps together and do them in time to the music."

The music started and Paula jerked me toward her. The one good thing about this kind of dance was that we were still far enough away from each other that I didn't have to talk to her. With a little luck I'd be back in the stands watching in a few minutes.

"Left, right, left-right-left," barked Mr. Murray. "Left, right, left-right-left. . . . Now swing." Paula started off slowly, but as the music got louder she swung harder. The faster she swung, the dizzier I got. At the apex[3] of the spin either she let go or my sweaty hands slipped away from hers. Either way I found myself spinning and twirling across the floor, straight for the punch bowl. The kids around us stopped to watch this whirling dervish. It seemed as if everyone was staring and pointing.

My left leg hit the table first, full force, causing it to tip forward. The strength of the blow caused my feet to slide out from under me and before I knew it I was on the ground and the table

3. **apex** [ā′ peks]: the highest point.

was on top of my legs. My pants were soaked with punch and my shirt was covered with smushed, smashed slivers of pretzels and potato chips.

There was almost complete silence until one of the kids started to laugh. Then everyone laughed. I felt stupid, dumb, and wet. I saw Mr. Murray running toward me to help, but Myron arrived first. I brushed myself off. He helped me stand up. I started to take a step, but my left leg refused to bear any weight and I collapsed in a heap.

The doctor at the hospital showed me the break in the X ray and told me my leg would be in a full leg cast for at least six weeks.

Since Myron came to the hospital with me, he was the first to sign my cast. He laughed the whole time he was writing. When he finished he said, "Read it."

What he wrote started at my thigh and went down the entire length of the cast. It said, "Remember what your dad said to you when you got out of the car? I know you're supposed to listen to your parents, but this is ridiculous." I looked up at Myron, who was still smiling. "Your cast will be off just in time for the Thanksgiving Dance. Going?"

JOEL SCHWARTZ

Joel Schwartz was born in 1940 in Philadelphia, Pennsylvania. His father was a doctor, and when Schwartz grew up he went to medical school too. After doing graduate work in psychiatry, Schwartz served as a medic in the Air Force. He came back to work and write in Pennsylvania.

Schwartz's first book, *Upchuck Summer,* was followed by a sequel called *Best Friends Don't Come in Three's,* and later by *Shrink*. Like all good writers, Schwartz believes in writing about what he knows. "My books," he says, "are about boys from a boy's point of view."

FOUNDERS OF THE CHILDREN'S RAIN FOREST

PHILLIP HOOSE

Children from the Fagervik School, Sweden

Forty first- and second-grade students from a small school in Sweden became upset when their teacher told them that rain forests[1] were being destroyed rapidly throughout the world. They wondered what they—so young, so few, and so far away from the tropics—could do that could really matter. Their answer has helped preserve rain forests around the world.

It all began in the first week of school when Eha Kern,[2] from the Fagervik[3] School, in the Swedish countryside, showed her forty first- and second-grade students pictures of hot, steamy jungles near the Equator. It was there, she said, that half the types of plants and animals in the whole world could be found. She read to them about monkeys

1. **rain forests:** very dense forests in regions, usually tropical, where rain is heavy all year.
2. **Eha Kern** [eʹ hä kärn]
3. **Fagervik** [fäʹ gär vēk]

and leopards and sloths,[4] about snakes that can paralyze your nerves with one bite, about strange plants that might hold a cure for cancer, about the great trees that give us oxygen to breathe and help keep the earth from becoming too hot.

And then she told them that the world's rain forests were being destroyed at the rate of one hundred acres a *minute*. In the past thirty years, she said, nearly half the world's rain forests have been cut down, often by poor people who burn the wood for fire. Sometimes forests are cleared to make pastures for cattle that are slaughtered and sold to hamburger chains in the U.S. and Europe. Sometimes the trees are sold and shipped away to make

4. **sloths** [slôths]: slow-moving mammals of South and Central America that live in trees and hang upside down from tree branches.

furniture and paper. More often they are just stacked up and burned. At this rate, there might not be any rain forests left in thirty years!

The children were horrified. The creatures of the rain forest could be gone before the students were even old enough to have a chance to see them. It didn't matter that they lived thousands of miles away in cold, snowy Sweden. It seemed to them that their future was being chopped and cleared away.

During the autumn, as the sunlight weakened and the days became short, the Fagervik children continued to think about the rain forest. Whenever they went on walks past the great fir trees on the school grounds, they imagined jaguars crouched in the limbs just above them, their long tails twitching impatiently.

They begged Mrs. Kern to help them think of something— anything—they could do to rescue the creatures of the tropics. And then one afternoon during a music lesson, a student named Roland Tiensuu asked suddenly, "Can't we just *buy* some rain forest?"

The lesson stopped. It was a simple, clear idea that all the others understood at once. The class began to cheer, and then they turned to their teacher. "Please, Mrs. Kern," they said. "Please, won't you find us a forest to buy?"

"PLEASE BUY MINE."

Mrs. Kern had no idea how to find a rain forest for sale. But then, the very weekend after Roland's idea, she was introduced to an American biologist[5] named Sharon Kinsman. As they chatted, Ms. Kinsman explained that she had been working in a rain forest called Monte Verde,[6] or Green Mountain.

When Mrs. Kern told Ms. Kinsman of the nearly impossible mission her students had given her, she expected the biologist to laugh. Instead her expression turned serious. "Oh," she said quickly, "please buy mine."

5. **biologist** [bī ol′ ə jist]: an expert in biology, which is the scientific study of plant and animal life.
6. **Monte Verde** [môn′ tā vār′ dā]

Ms. Kinsman said that some people in Monte Verde were trying desperately to buy land so that more trees wouldn't be cut. Much land had already been protected, but much more was needed. Land was cheap there, she said—only about twenty-five dollars per acre.

Ms. Kinsman agreed to visit the Fagervik School. She would bring a map and slides of the Monte Verde forest and tell the children where they could send money to buy rain forest land. When Mrs. Kern told the children what had happened, they didn't even seem surprised. As they put it, "We knew you would find one."

"THERE ARE NO BAD IDEAS."

In the days before Sharon Kinsman's visit, the Fagervik students began to think about how to raise money. They asked Mrs. Kern to write down all their ideas. As she picked up a piece of chalk, several children spoke at once.

"Pony rides!"

"Let's collect old things and sell them!"

"What about a rain forest evening here at school?"

"Dog washing!"

Dog washing? They began to laugh. "That would never work," someone said. "Who would give money for that?" Mrs. Kern put her chalk down. "Look," she said. "Let's make this our rule: there are no bad ideas. The only bad thing is if you have an idea and don't say it. Then we can't use it." She returned to the blackboard. Were there more ideas?

"A rabbit jumping contest!"

"Rabbit jumping?" said Mrs. Kern. "Be serious. You can't *make* a rabbit jump."

"Oh, yes, we all have rabbits. We can train them. We can. We *can!*"

Mrs. Kern tried to imagine someone actually paying money to watch children try to make rabbits jump. She couldn't. This idea was crazy.

"Mrs. Kern . . . there's no such thing as a bad idea . . . remember?" She did. "Rabbit jumping," she wrote, dutifully putting her doubts aside.

GIANT SPIDERS AND DEADLY SNAKES

On November 6, 1987, Sharon Kinsman arrived at the Fagervik School. She was just as enthusiastic as the students. They put on skits for her about rain forests and showed her the many books they had written about tropical creatures. Then at last, it was her turn to show them slides of the Monte Verde forest.

First she unfolded a map of the forest and pointed to the area their money could preserve from cutting. She told them that 400 bird species live in the forest, more than in all of Sweden, as well as 490 kinds of butterflies and 500 types of trees.

Monte Verde is also the only home in

the world, she said, for the golden toad, a creature that seems to glow in the dark.

Then she showed her slides. As the room became dark, the students were swept into a hot, steamy jungle half the world away. The slides took them sloshing along a narrow, muddy trail, crisscrossed with roots and vines. A dark canopy of giant trees, thick with bright flowering plants, closed in above them.

They saw giant spiders and deadly snakes. Ms. Kinsman's tape recorder made the forest ring with the shriek of howler monkeys calling to each other and with the chattering of parrots above the trees. They saw the golden toad, the scarlet macaw, and the red-backed poison-arrow frog.

And they saw the forest disappearing, too. They saw hard-muscled men, their backs glistening with sweat, pushing chain saws deep into the giant trees. They could almost smell the smoke of burning tree limbs and feel the thunder of thick, brown trunks crashing down. Behind great piles of ragged wood, the tropical sky was hazy with smoke. Time seemed very short.

When the lights came on, the students were back in Sweden, but they were not the same. Now they had seen their forest—and the danger it faced. There was no time to lose. Mrs. Kern had inspired them with a problem, and Roland had given them an idea they could work with. Sharon Kinsman had shown them their target. Now it was up to them.

"WE KNEW WHAT WE WANTED."

Two weeks later, more than a hundred people crowded into an old schoolhouse near the Fagervik School for a rain forest evening. Students stood by the door and collected ten crowns (about $1.50) from each person. Special programs cost another crown. Even though it was winter, rain splattered steadily onto the roof, just as it must have been raining in the Monte Verde forest. To the students, rain was a good sign.

First they performed a play containing a dramatic scene in which trees of the rain forest were cut and creatures killed. That way guests would understand the problem they were trying to help solve. As the applause died down, the children passed an old hat around, urging audience members to drop money in it.

Then they sold rain forest books and rain forest poems. "We were not afraid to ask for money," remembers Maria Karlsson, who was nine. "We knew what we wanted was important." One boy stood at a table keeping track of how much they were making. Whenever a classmate would hand over a fresh delivery of cash, he would count it quickly and shout above the noise, "Now we've got two hundred crowns!!" "Now it's three hundred!!"

The evening's total came to 1,600 crowns, or about $240. The next day, they figured out that they had raised enough money to save about twelve football fields worth of rain forest. It was wonderful . . . but was it enough space for a sloth? A leopard? They all knew the answer. They needed more.

They filled up another blackboard with ideas and tried them out. Everything seemed to work. Mrs. Kern brought in a list of prominent people who might make donations. Two girls wrote a letter to the richest woman on the list. A few days later, a check arrived. Someone else wrote to the king of Sweden and asked if he would watch them perform plays about the rain forest. He said yes.

One day they went to a recording studio and made a tape of their rain forest songs. From the very beginning, Mrs. Kern and a music teacher had been helping them write songs. They started with old melodies they liked, changing them a little as they went along. As soon as anybody came up with a good line, they sang it into a tape recorder so they wouldn't forget it by the end of the song. They rehearsed the songs many times on their school bus before recording them, then designed a cover and used some of their money to buy plastic boxes for the tapes. Within months, they had sold five hundred tapes at ten dollars each.

The more they used their imaginations, the more money they raised. They decided to have a fair. "We had a magician and charged admission," remembers Lia Degeby, who was eight. "We charged to see who could make the ugliest face. We had a pony riding contest. We had a market. We had a lady with a beard. We had the strongest lady in the world. Maria forecast the future in a cabin. We tried everything." The biggest money maker of all was the rabbit jumping contest, even though each rabbit sat still when its time came to jump! Even carrots couldn't budge them. One simply flopped over and went to sleep, crushing its necklace of flowers.

Soon they needed a place to put all the money they had earned. Mrs. Kern's husband, Bernd, helped them form an organization called Barnens Regnskog,[7] which means Children's Rain Forest. They opened a bank account with a post office box where people could continue to mail donations.

By midwinter, they had raised $1,400. The children addressed an envelope to the Monte Verde Cloud Forest Protection League, folded a check inside, and sent it on its way to Costa Rica.[8] Weeks later, they received a crumpled package covered with brightly colored stamps. It contained a map of the area that had been bought with their money. A grateful writer thanked them for saving nearly ninety acres of Costa Rican rain forest.

In the early spring, the Fagervik students performed at the Swedish Children's Fair, which led to several national television appearances. Soon schools from all over Sweden were joining Barnens Regnskog and sending money to Monte Verde. At one high school

7. **Barnens Regnskog** [bär′ nenz rän′ skog]
8. **Costa Rica** [kos′ tə rē′ kə]: country in Central America, northwest of Panama.

near Stockholm, two thousand students did chores all day in the city and raised nearly $15,000. And inspired by the students, the Swedish government gave a grant of $80,000 to Monte Verde.

"I Think of My Future."

After another year's work, the children of Fagervik had raised $25,000 more. The families who could afford it sent their children to Costa Rica to see Monte Verde. Just before Christmas, ten Fagervik children stepped off the plane, blinking in the bright Costa Rican sunlight. It was hot! They stripped off their coats and sweaters, piled into a bus, and headed for the mountains.

A few hours later, the bus turned onto a narrow, rocky road that threaded its way through steep mountains. The children looked out upon spectacular waterfalls that fell hundreds of feet. Occasionally they glimpsed monkeys swinging through the trees.

Ahead, the mountaintops disappeared inside a dark purple cloud. For a few moments they could see five rainbows at once. Soon it began to rain.

The next morning, they joined ten Costa Rican children and went on a hike through the Monte Verde rain forest. Sometimes the thick mud made them step right out of their boots. But it didn't matter. "There were plants everywhere," says Lia. "I saw monkeys and flowers."

On Christmas day, the children of the Fagervik School proudly presented the staff of the Monte Verde Cloud Forest with their check for $25,000. They said it was a holiday present for all the children of the world.

The Monte Verde Conservation League used their gift, and funds that had been donated by other children previously, to establish what is now known as El Bosque Eterno de los Niños,[9] or the Eternal International Children's Rain Forest. It is a living monument to the caring and power of young people everywhere. So far, kids from twenty-one nations have raised more than two million dollars to preserve nearly 33,000 acres of rain forest, plenty of room for jaguars and ocelots[10] and tapirs.[11] The first group of Fagervik students have now graduated to another school, but the first- and second-graders who have replaced them are still raising great sums of money. The school total is now well over $50,000.

The Fagervik students continue to amaze their teacher. "I never thought they could do so much," Mrs. Kern says. "Sometimes I say to them, 'Why do you work so hard?' They say, 'I think of my future.' They make me feel optimistic. When I am with them, I think maybe anything can be done."

9. **El Bosque Eterno de los Niños** [el bos′ kā ā tār′ nō dā lōs nē′ nyōs]
10. **ocelots** [os′ ə lotz]: spotted cats smaller than leopards.
11. **tapirs** [tā′ pərz]: large piglike animals of tropical America with hooves and a flexible snout.

My name is Roy Vargas Garcia. I am twelve years old. I live in a small community called La Cruz de Abangares,[12] in Costa Rica. There are seven in my family. My father is a dairyman, my mother a housewife.

I love to listen to the songs of birds and insects of the forest. Often I see sloths, gray foxes, armadillos, opossums, birds, monkeys, and butterflies. The climate here is cool, and trees are tall and green, with many mosses.

I am very pleased that other children from around the world want to protect our forest. I want children to know that we who live here are protecting it, too.

In the past, our farmers cut the forest. Not because they did not care about it, but because they needed to make their farms and their vegetable gardens and to get firewood and lumber and so to raise their children.

But now many farmers are planting trees in windbreaks on the farms. In my community we are buying a small piece of land we call a community reserve to protect where our water comes from. We are doing this with help and training from the Monte Verde Conservation League.

I want to thank all the children who are helping save forests. Thank you.

Roy Vargas Garcia

12. **La Cruz de Abangares** [lä krüs dā ä bän gä′ räs]

PHILLIP HOOSE

Phillip Hoose was born in 1947 in South Bend, Indiana. Like many young people, Hoose grew up seeing things in the world that he thought were wrong and felt powerless to fix them. It was only when he had children of his own that he realized how badly "kids are underestimated by adults." He was amazed when his kindergarten-aged daughter helped figure out a way to raise money to help homeless people. Her experience gave him the idea for *It's Our World, Too!*

Beni Seballos

PHILLIP HOOSE

*V*olunteering to take care of others can be just as important to a community as standing up to an injustice. It can be just as challenging, too. Beni Seballos of Racida, California, overcame her self-doubt and volunteered to take care of older people with diseases that affect their ability to think, remember, and move. The things she learned gave her confidence and helped her solve one of the biggest problems in her own life.

One day when she was fifteen, Beni Seballos stepped onto a plane with ten of her aunts, uncles, cousins, nieces, and nephews and said good-bye to everything she loved. Soon her home, her friends, and her school in the Philippines were far behind her.

When they arrived in Los Angeles, they drove to a small house. There they would stay with her aunt and grandparents until they could find enough money to buy a home of their own.

The fourteen of them tried their best to be cheerful. For Beni, the hardest part was trying to get along with her grandmother. She was a stern, quiet woman, used to the respect that elders commanded in the Philippines. Beni was noisy and opinionated. Her grandmother always seemed to disapprove of her. Each day Beni would ask her grandmother if she could help with dinner, and the answer was always no. That "no" filled the kitchen, leaving no space for Beni. She always left the room in anger, wondering how long she could take living there.

Racida High School was no better. She didn't know anybody at first. She made the basketball team but rarely got in the games. "Academic Decathlon was even worse," Beni recalls. "A team of kids from Racida High tried to answer questions faster than a team from another school. It wasn't about learning. All they wanted to do was kick butt. I hated it."

The one thing she really liked was a volunteer organization called Youth Community Services, or YCS. After hearing about it at school, Beni went on a weekend field trip to plant trees in a farm area. There was no feeling of competition here. Everyone was working together. She volunteered for YCS at a blood bank, at a recycling center, and with a program that helped keep young kids off drugs. At last, she was having fun in the United States.

Her parents didn't understand. To them, volunteering just kept her away from home. She wasn't even getting school credit for it. When Beni put on her jacket to go to a YCS event, her grandmother would glare, and her mother would say, softly but pointedly, "Oh, you're going off again, aren't you, Beni?"

During the summer break, a YCS counselor urged Beni to volunteer at a senior citizens center. The staff needed volunteers to help take care of old people who had Alzheimer's and Parkinson's diseases. Think of all you could learn, the counselor kept saying.

Beni wasn't so sure. She found herself wondering what a sixteen-year-old could really have in common with someone who was seventy-five or eighty. She hated to admit it to herself, but old people sounded boring. Even worse, what if they all treated her the way her grandmother did?

But maybe the counselor was right. After all, she thought, you learn most by doing what you understand least. Beni signed up for four days a week, five hours a day, and then walked to the library to find out about Alzheimer's and Parkinson's diseases.

A medical encyclopedia said that both diseases affect the brain's ability to function. Alzheimer's patients gradually lose their memories, and Parkinson's patients gradually lose control of their muscles. After reading less than a page, Beni closed the book, unable to go on. "I was terrified," she remembers. "I could see myself having to force-feed these drooling people. I'd have to pick them up off the ground all the time. I thought they'd be vegetables.

"I practically ran out of the library. I was ready to quit before I had ever met a single patient. By the time I got home, I was wondering, 'What did I get myself into?'"

"What Do You Think About This?"

The first day, Beni introduced herself to the center's supervisor, Kathleen, and the six other volunteers, all in their forties and fifties. They were friendly, but she wondered if they really believed a teenager could handle the work.

Kathleen explained that the volunteers were supposed to feed the patients, take them for walks, and help give them their medicine. She went over each patient's medicine and diet. She kept looking at Beni and saying, "Don't worry, you'll do fine."

Then Kathleen opened the door, and they all walked out into the hallway, where about fifteen patients and their relatives were waiting. Some patients were in wheelchairs. Others were in walkers. A few leaned on canes.

Beni hung back and watched as the other volunteers rushed forward to greet the patients. Was she supposed to help them into their wheelchairs? How did you do it, anyway? What if she dropped someone? "I could see some of the patients' relatives looking at me. I felt them thinking, She's just a kid. She doesn't look like she knows what she's doing."

She followed the crowd into a big room, where the volunteers were supposed to serve the patients coffee and doughnuts. Beni's mind went blank. She couldn't remember who was supposed to have only half a doughnut and who wasn't supposed to get a doughnut at all. Kathleen was nowhere in sight. Beni fought back tears. This was terrible. It was the Alzheimer's patients who were supposed to have memory problems, not her.

After coffee, Kathleen was reading a newspaper article to a group of patients when one of them interrupted. He pointed to Beni. "You're a young person," he said. "What do you think about this?" Beni was startled. An older person actually wanted her opinion? This was certainly different from home. Well, actually she *did* have an opinion on the topic of the article, and so she gave it. They listened carefully and discussed it. This part isn't so bad, Beni thought.

She went home that night exhausted and determined to do better tomorrow. As always, her grandmother was in the kitchen. They went through the usual routine again, with Beni offering to help and her grandmother refusing her. Beni walked out fuming. She had to get out of there.

The next morning, Beni went to the center early and memorized the patients' names. When the patients arrived, she sat down beside a frail woman named Lil with a sparse crown of thin white hair. Beni peeled an orange for her and filled up her cup of coffee halfway with a single lump of sugar, just as Lil's chart said. As she was working, Beni told Lil about what it had been like to move from the Philippines.

Lil began to talk, too. She said she had spent much of her life raising five wonderful children.

"Where are they now?" Beni asked.

"Who?"

"Your children."

"What?"

"Your children. You were saying you have five children."

Lil wrung the hem of her dress in her hands, looking frantically around the room. "What do you mean? I-I-I can't remember." She seemed to be growing more desperate by the second. Beni quickly changed the subject to her own college plans, and gradually Lil relaxed. It was Beni's first real contact with Alzheimer's disease. It taught her that she had to listen and be flexible, alert to each patient's needs. Patients wouldn't always be able to stick to the same subject for very long.

Later that week, Beni was leading a patient named Oscar outside for a game of shuffleboard when she heard the sharp scrape of metal behind her. His walker had become caught between two chairs. Trembling, he tried to shake loose. Beni knelt to pry the walker free, but it was no use. Oscar was growing enraged and started to shout. His face was turning red. Here it is, Beni thought, the emergency I can't handle. She sprinted into the kitchen to get help. Three volunteers and Kathy rushed out, and in a moment, they had him free. "You handled it well," Kathy said to Beni later. "Just get help."

As the summer went by, Beni faced many different kinds of challenges. A few patients tried to wander off. Some became angry because they couldn't remember when to take their medicine. One refused to go back inside after a walk.

After a few weeks at the center, Beni found herself thinking differently about the patients. She could no longer think of them as "old people" or "senior citizens," or "Alzheimer's patients" or even "patients." They had become individuals, like her, who just happened to be at a different stage of their lives. Like her, they all had their own interests and families, hopes and fears, opinions and problems.

She discovered that if she listened carefully, she could find something in common with almost everyone. Alex wrote poetry, just like Beni. Sometimes at the shuffleboard court, they recited their poems to each other. Beni and Oscar spoke Spanish together. Blackie told her World War II stories. Mary taught her a few words of Czech. Lil loved to talk about children.

By the end of the summer, it seemed to Beni that being young had been an advantage, not a handicap, at the center. "I was special to some of the Alzheimer's patients," she says. "I think maybe having me around helped them remember how they were when they were young themselves."

BEANS AND FRIENDSHIP

In September, Beni said a tearful good-bye to the patients and staff and took a week off before school started. She had some unfinished business.

All summer long, things had gotten worse and worse with her grandmother until finally she had moved out of her aunt's house in order to find some peace in her life. But she didn't feel at peace. She loved her grandmother, and she wanted to put things right between them.

For a while it had seemed strange that she could have fun with Lil or Oscar or Alex but not her own grandmother. Then it came to her: When things got tough with a patient at the center, she kept trying patiently until she found a way to get through. But when things got tough with her grandmother, she gave up.

So one afternoon, she walked over to her aunt's house, determined to treat her grandmother as she had learned to treat the people at the center.

As usual, Beni's grandmother was in the kitchen. "Hi," Beni said. "Is there anything I can do?" "No," said her grandmother. This time Beni didn't leave. She noticed a bowl of string beans on the counter and carried them to the kitchen table. She sat down, picked up a bean, and snapped off the end.

She began to tell her grandmother about her summer. Though her grandmother didn't say anything, Beni could sense that she was listening. After a while, her grandmother wiped her hands on a towel, pulled up a chair, and sat down at the other end of the table. She picked up a bean and snapped the top off. A half hour later, there was a big pile of beans between them—and the beginning of a friendship.

Beni says that friendship was maybe the greatest gift of the summer. It couldn't have happened until she herself changed, and volunteering at the center was the key that opened doors within her. "The summer started working for me when I began to share myself with the patients, not just log time," she says. "Then it was fun. I know I did a good job at the center, but I probably got more out of it than the patients. I learned that caring is like a muscle. The more you exercise it, the more you *can* share."

I FEEL MYSELF
    GROW OLD
MY EYES GO BLIND
    MY HANDS SHAKE
PLEASE LORD, LET
    SOMEONE ALSO
    HELP ME OUT
WHEN TOMORROW'S DAWNS
    GROW DARK ON
    ME.
          —Beni Seballos

PHILLIP HOOSE

Phillip Hoose was born in 1947 in South Bend, Indiana. Like many young people, Hoose grew up seeing things in the world that he thought were wrong and felt powerless to fix them. It was only when he had children of his own that he realized how badly "kids are underestimated by adults." He was amazed when his kindergarten-aged daughter helped figure out a way to raise money to help homeless people. Her experience gave him the idea for *It's Our World, Too!*

For the book, Hoose conducted nearly a hundred interviews with young people who had taken action to help others. "I wish I'd had a book like this when I was a kid," Hoose says, "or known people like the kids I interviewed. I would have felt less alone."

THE FUN THEY HAD

Margie even wrote about it that night in her diary. On the page headed May 17, 2157, she wrote, "Today Tommy found a real book!"

It was a very old book. Margie's grandfather once said that when he was a little boy *his* grandfather told him that there was a time when all stories were printed on paper.

They turned the pages, which were yellow and crinkly, and it was awfully funny to read words that stood still instead of moving the way they were supposed to— on a screen, you know. And then, when they turned back to the page before, it had the same words on it that it had had when they read it the first time.

"Gee," said Tommy, "what a waste. When you're through with the book, you just throw it away, I guess. Our television screen must have had a million books on it and it's good for plenty more. I wouldn't throw *it* away."

"Same with mine," said Margie. She was eleven and hadn't seen as many telebooks as Tommy had. He was thirteen.

She said, "Where did you find it?"

"In my house." He pointed without looking, because he was busy reading. "In the attic."

"What's it about?"

"School."

Margie was scornful. "School? What's there to write about school? I hate school."

Margie always hated school, but now she hated it more than ever. The mechanical teacher had been giving her test after test in geography and she had been doing worse and worse until her mother had shaken her head sorrowfully and sent for the County Inspector.

He was a round little man with a red face and a whole box of tools with dials and wires. He smiled at Margie and gave her an apple, then took the teacher apart. Margie had hoped he wouldn't know how to put it together again, but he knew how all right, and, after an hour or so, there it was again, large and black and ugly, with a big screen on which all the lessons were shown and the questions were asked. That wasn't so bad. The part Margie hated most was the slot where she had to put homework and test papers. She always had to write them out in a punch code they made her learn when she was six years old, and the mechanical teacher calculated the mark in no time.

The Inspector had smiled after he was finished and patted Margie's head. He said to her mother, "It's not the little girl's fault, Mrs. Jones. I think the geography sector was geared a little too quick. Those things happen sometimes. I've slowed it up to an average ten-year level. Actually, the over-all pattern of her progress is quite satisfactory." And he patted Margie's head again.

Margie was disappointed. She had been hoping they would take the teacher away altogether. They had once taken Tommy's teacher away for nearly a month because the history sector had blanked out completely.

So she said to Tommy, "Why would anyone write about school?"

Tommy looked at her with very superior eyes. "Because it's not our kind of school, stupid. This is the old kind of school that they had hundreds and hundreds of years ago." He added loftily, pronouncing the word carefully, *"Centuries* ago."

Margie was hurt. "Well, I don't know what kind of school they had all that time ago." She read the book over his shoulder for a while, then said, "Anyway, they had a teacher."

"Sure they had a teacher, but it wasn't a *regular* teacher. It was a man."

"A man? How could a man be a teacher?"

"Well, he just told the boys and girls things and gave them homework and asked them questions."

"A man isn't smart enough."

"Sure he is. My father knows as much as my teacher."

"He can't. A man can't know as much as a teacher."

"He knows almost as much, I betcha."

Margie wasn't prepared to dispute that. She said, "I wouldn't want a strange man in my house to teach me."

Tommy screamed with laughter. "You don't know much, Margie. The teachers didn't live in the house. They had a special building and all the kids went there."

"And all the kids learned the same thing?"

"Sure, if they were the same age."

"But my mother says a teacher has to be adjusted to fit the mind of each boy and girl it teaches and that each kid has to be taught differently."

"Just the same they didn't do it that way then. If you don't like it, you don't have to read the book."

"I didn't say I didn't like it," Margie said quickly. She wanted to read about those funny schools.

They weren't even half-finished when Margie's mother called, "Margie! School!"

Margie looked up. "Not yet, Mamma."

"Now!" said Mrs. Jones. "And it's probably time for Tommy, too."

Margie said to Tommy, "Can I read the book some more with you after school?"

"Maybe," he said nonchalantly.[1] He walked away whistling, the dusty old book tucked beneath his arm.

Margie went into the schoolroom. It was right next to her bedroom, and the mechanical teacher was on and waiting for her. It was always on at the same time every day except Saturday and Sunday, because her mother said little girls learned better if they learned at regular hours.

The screen was lit up, and it said: "Today's arithmetic lesson is on the addition of proper fractions. Please insert yesterday's homework in the proper slot."

Margie did so with a sigh. She was thinking about the old schools they had when her grandfather's grandfather was a little boy. All the kids from the whole neighborhood came, laughing and shouting in the schoolyard, sitting together in the schoolroom, going home together at the end of the day. They learned the same things, so they could help one another on the homework and talk about it.

And the teachers were people. . . .

The mechanical teacher was flashing on the screen: "When we add the fractions 1/2 and 1/4—"

Margie was thinking about how the kids must have loved it in the old days. She was thinking about the fun they had.

1. **nonchalantly** [non´ shə länt´ lē]: indifferently, casually.

ISAAC ASIMOV

Isaac Asimov [1920-1992] was born in Petrovichi, U.S.S.R., and came to the United States when he was three years old. He grew up in Brooklyn, New York, where his family had a candy store. He discovered science fiction through magazines for sale on the store's newsstand.

At seventeen, he wrote his first science fiction story, "The Cosmic Corkscrew." Later he became one of the best-known science fiction writers in the world. His last books include *The Asimov Chronicles* and *Robot Visions.*

Something

from *Children of the Dust Bowl*

JERRY STANLEY

On a bright September morning in 1940 the Kern County[1] superintendent of education waved good-bye to his wife and left for work. On this day, instead of his usual coat and tie, Leo Hart was wearing old overalls and work boots. Leo told Edna he would be home late, but she already knew that. They had talked about this special day for weeks and had worked for it for months.

Leo drove the flatbed truck[2] to the field next to Weedpatch Camp. On the odd-looking stretch of land marked by piles of bricks, boards, and boxes of whatnot, Leo met with the teachers he had hired and introduced them to the fifty children from Weedpatch Camp whose parents had agreed to let Leo have them for the day. Then he told them all to get to work. They did. Brick by brick, board by board, the children of the Dust Bowl, eight teachers, and Leo Hart built Weedpatch School.

On the first day a team of children dug a hundred-yard trench from the water tower in the camp to the condemned buildings in the

1. **Kern County** [kern]: California county in the San Joaquin Valley where Weedpatch Camp and other farm-labor camps were located.
2. **flatbed truck:** truck with flat back section for carrying items.

to Watch

field. They laid a three-quarter-inch pipe in the trench, and on the second day the school had running water. Teachers instructed the children on hygiene, while Leo and some of the boys dug two huge holes in the ground and built two outhouses. After that, Leo said, "All the children used them."

"It was something to watch," Leo remembered. "It was the first time where they were working for something of their own. It was the first time where they could be proud of who they were and what they were doing." Pete Bancroft, the newly hired principal of the school, worked side by side with the teachers and the Okie kids, building the school and instilling in the Dust Bowl children a spirit of confidence and self-worth. "There was no partiality," Leo said, "no embarrassment or ridicule." Instead, "There was friendship, understanding, guidance, and love."

As the weeks stretched into months, the school rose from the field. Within two months the two condemned buildings had been renovated and made into four general-purpose classrooms. Following that, the twenty-five thousand bricks donated by the National Youth Authority were turned into three more classrooms and a cafeteria. This took an additional three months. A home economics building was needed. No problem. An old railroad car was located and moved to the school, where the boys added plumbing and wiring, and remodeled its interior. A shop building where mechanics and other trades could be learned was also needed. No problem. Leo persuaded the district to donate an abandoned auditorium, which was disassembled, hauled to the school, and remanufactured into a shop room. The Okie children learned a dozen useful trades—including plumbing, electrical wiring, carpentry, plastering, and masonry.[3] Scrap lumber was sawed into bookshelves. Discarded sinks were fixed in place for a chemistry lab. Orange crates and wooden boxes were fashioned into chairs, desks, and tables.

There was more. By October the field was alive with the sound of a dozen hoes and clattering farm machinery striking hard earth. The Okie children plowed part of the school field and planted vegetables and other crops. "Edna said we should start with potatoes and so we did," Leo recalled. "Potatoes and alfalfa. Tomatoes, carrots, celery, corn, and watermelon. The children especially liked the watermelon." Toiling in the sun for hours, tilling, planting, weeding, and harvesting was welcome labor to children who could still remember the taste of apple seeds, carrot stems, and coffee grounds.

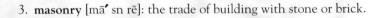

The Okie kids also raised their own livestock. They built pens for sheep, pigs, chickens, and cows and dug a basement to store slaughtered livestock. Sometime in December 1940 a local butcher heard about "the Okie school" and

3. **masonry** [mā′ sn rē]: the trade of building with stone or brick.

wandered out to the site. The man spent ten hours at the school that day slaughtering pigs and cows and instructing the children until they learned the basic skills of a butcher.

During the early months of the school, Edna Hart helped the women at Weedpatch Camp cook meals for the children. But by the time Edna went to work in the school's new cafeteria in the spring of 1941, the school had become completely self-sufficient in potatoes, vegetables, milk, eggs, and beef.

The teachers, Leo said, "went out of their way to help these children and teach them things about themselves and the world that they couldn't learn anywhere else." Jim McPherson taught the Okie children history, geography, math, science—and shoe cobbling, so they could repair their parents' shoes. Rose Gilger taught them science, typing—and sewing, so their families didn't have to wear oversize clothes or rags. Chemistry teacher Barbara Sabovitch even taught the girls how to make face cream, rouge, and lipstick—in a chemistry lab!

Principal Pete Bancroft bought a C-46[4] airplane from military surplus for two hundred dollars and had it carted to the school. "I taught them aircraft mechanics," Pete said, "and if they maintained a grade of 90 percent or better in arithmetic, I let them drive the plane down the makeshift runway and back." Both Pete and Leo enrolled their own children in the school and Pete brought a doctor and nurse out to care for sick children. Pete dispensed cod-liver oil and orange juice until the first crops came in and the school cafeteria was built. Rose Gilger and Beverly Ahrens worked in that cafeteria as well as in the classroom and, like the other teachers, took the Okie children into Bakersfield on Sundays to go to church and to accept donations of food and clothing from local merchants and the Salvation Army. Other teachers—Edith Houghan, for instance—spent weekends at the school with children who were sick, because, Edith said, "They were better off in the nurse's room than at home in their one-room huts."

Fred Smith heard about the school and applied for a job as a music teacher. Leo only had enough money to hire Fred for one day a week, but Fred usually worked on weekends for nothing. When Leo sent Fred his yearly check of six hundred dollars, Fred sent it back.

Determination and a lot of hard work combined to change the fate of the Okie children from Weedpatch Camp. As discards and donations were slowly turned into a school, the children came to believe that anything was possible—and none of them doubted this after Leo picked up a shovel one day and started to dig at the east end of the field between the school and the camp. When twelve-year-old Bob Farley asked Leo what he was digging, Leo said, "Swimming pool."

4. **C-46**: a military airplane of the 1940s.

If the migrant[5] children did not "goof off," Leo said, "if they kept up on their academics," he would let them dig in their spare time. "Dig in the hole," the children called it.

"We used the twelve-by-twelve forms that were the floors of the tents over in the camp and built a wall around the inside," Leo recalled. "We poured concrete walls and a deck all the way around."

Leo made a game out of building the swimming pool during recess and after school. He helped the children set the frames and lay reinforcement rods. Then two, sometimes three wheelbarrows would be filled with cement, and Leo and the children would race the wheelbarrows to the hole in four-person teams. "The hole" became the first public swimming pool in Kern County.

When the swimming pool was finished, Elyse Phillips recalled, she pinched her nose and fell face forward into the water, "crying because I was so happy."

5. **migrant** [miʹ grənt]: person who moves from place to place, especially for farm work.

Our School

While the children of Weedpatch Camp were building a school for themselves, they were also attending classes, doing homework, and taking tests on a regular basis. Besides practical training in aircraft mechanics, sewing, cobbling, and canning fruits and vegetables, they learned the basic subjects taught in elementary school and junior high: English, arithmetic, geography, history. As many as two hundred students aged between six and sixteen attended the school during its first year of operation, from September 1940 to May 1941.

Their day was divided into two three-hour periods. Half the children went to classes in the morning, normally from nine A.M. until noon, while the other half worked on building the school and tending the crops. After lunch, the groups switched places.

But it is impossible to describe a "normal" day at Weedpatch School. For example, in October 1940, twelve-year-old Doyle Powers from Ardmore, Oklahoma, was studying arithmetic with others in an unfinished classroom, which was framed with two-by-fours[6] but had no roof. Suddenly, "The sky fell in on us. It started to rain, and classes were canceled for two days until the storm passed." In November a severe dust storm forced suspension of classes in one unfinished building when two of its walls collapsed. Della Stewart, from Duncan, Oklahoma, who was eleven, remembered missing school for nearly two weeks when her family found temporary employment in the fields of Tulare County, north of Kern. Instead of attending school every day, some children had to baby-sit siblings in the camp while adult members of the family worked.

Because attendance at the school was sometimes sporadic[7] and because many students were learning from scratch, Leo recalled "There were no quantum leaps in knowledge. There were only little victories, when a student understood addition or learned to write a complete sentence. But the main thing was they were learning." And they were. As weeks stretched into months and months into years, addition led to subtraction, English led to literature, and American history led to world history.

For some students at Weedpatch School, education had an immediate practical effect. For example, Joyce Foster lived with her parents and two younger brothers in two tents in Weedpatch Camp for more than three years. Joyce was ten in 1941 when she started attending the school. She was twelve when her father, thirty-six-year-old Roy Foster from Clinton, Oklahoma, contracted a lung disease while working grapes and died. Joyce cried for weeks because she

6. **two-by-fours**: pieces of lumber four inches wide and two inches thick used in building.
7. **sporadic** [spə rad′ ik]: occasional, happening at uneven intervals.

missed her father. She was appointed the task of writing a letter to relatives in Clinton conveying the sad news. She was the only member of her family who could write.

Joyce also wrote an essay about her father and read it aloud to the Okie families gathered in the auditorium at Weedpatch Camp. The Okie school children sometimes read stories and poems before the dances on Saturday nights, but it was a special moment when Joyce stood on the makeshift bandstand. She remembered riding with her father on a tractor in Clinton and picking beans with him in Arizona. And as she recalled each memory she thanked her father for giving his family food, shelter, and love. Her essay was called "An Okie Man" and it was composed in an English class at Weedpatch School.

At the same time, the children who studied at Weedpatch School had life experiences they would never forget. Patsy Lamb told the story of the first Thanksgiving at the school. Leo, Edna, and the teachers prepared a turkey dinner for the children. "Mrs. Hunter told us all to go to this one big room. We were so happy," Patsy recalled. But "when we sat down and tried to eat the turkey, most of us couldn't. We never had turkey before. We didn't like the taste. We pushed the food around on our plates. Later we got some beans from the camp and we ate beans for our Thanksgiving dinner."

Other students have vivid memories of the outings at the school. On Saturdays, for students who had shown improvement and for those who scored 90 percent or better in arithmetic for the week, Leo and the teachers took the children on one-day vacations, which Leo called "outings." Nathan Reed, twelve years old out of Guymon in the Panhandle,[8] which had few lakes or streams, caught his first fish on an outing in the Kern River Canyon. Leo's flatbed truck carried a dozen Okie children that day. The catfish were spawning in the shallows below the banks of the wild Kern River, and all of the children caught fish by hand-casting ten-foot lengths of string with hooks and

8. **Panhandle** [pan′ han dl]: a narrow stretch of land connected to a larger section of land, such as the Texas Panhandle.

worms attached. On that day, Nathan recalled, "We stayed out too long and it started to rain. It rained so hard that the truck sunk down to its frame in the mud when we got on it. We all piled off and dug it out with our bare hands while it poured cats and dogs." The children were soaked and covered with mud, and so was Leo. It was a memorable end to "a great day," and Nathan was hooked on fishing for life.

Students remember a thousand other "great days" at Weedpatch School. There was the day Edna gave Beth Stewart her first pair of earrings, and the day Beth made her first dress in sewing class for her mother. There was the day Doyle Powers got 92 percent on his arithmetic test and got to taxi the C-46 down the runway and back. There was the day when the school's first crop of potatoes came in and sold for two hundred fifty dollars. Most of the money went toward building the cafeteria, but fifty dollars was used for a trip to the Kern County Fair in Bakersfield, where over one hundred kids, Leo estimated, rode the Ferris wheel and the merry-go-round—and ate ice cream! A year later, Eddie Davis's hand-raised hog, "Eddie," placed third at the fair, but that's not what made that day special. The highlight of the day came when another boy, taller than Eddie, called Eddie a dumb Okie and Eddie stood up for himself. Eddie punched the boy in the nose and knocked him into the hog slop.

Eddie was also present during what came to be known as the Fight. It was a Saturday, and most of the parents of Weedpatch Camp were working in the fields. Perhaps as many as fifty children were playing baseball at the school or swimming in the pool when three cars driven by teenage boys began to circle the playground. The teenage boys got out of the cars and squared off in front of Eddie and a line of other sixteen-year-old boys from the camp. When the intruders hurled rocks into the swimming pool, the Okie boys charged forward and the Fight was on. Some men from the camp rushed over to the playground to restore order, but by then the invaders were in retreat with bloody noses and scuffed faces. That was what the Okie children meant when they said, "It was *our school*."

"When we started to build the school, it gave the parents hope," Leo said. "They could see what the school meant to the children.

They could see it every day in their faces, in their laughter. And the longer we ran the school, the longer the families stayed. The greater portion of them stayed there and would stay the year round and work so their kids could stay in this school. They understood what we were trying to do. It was the first time the children ever had anything of their own, where all the attention was on them, where they were given the best and they knew everyone was for them." Teacher Mariel Hunter recalled a girl in the eighth grade whose family was about to move away. The girl wanted to stay in school so badly and go on to high school that she planned to marry so she could stay in town. Mariel took the problem to Leo, and Leo found the girl a home where she could live in return for doing household chores.

"Everyone pitched in to make it grow," Mariel said. "We all worked together like one big family, and grow we did together. . . . The kids appreciated everything you did for them because they had so little to light up their lives."

"The teachers made us feel important and like someone really cared," Trice Masters said. "The school gave us pride and dignity and honor when we didn't have those things. It was *our school*. It did a great deal to cause us to believe we were special."

Bob Rutledge was fourteen when his family moved into the camp. He spoke for his classmates while studying old photos of Weedpatch School. "Look at these people," he said. "They're not dumb." He spoke of poverty as being "in the mind" and said, "We never accepted poverty." He described the "Okie attitude" at the school as "This is what we are now, but it's not what we're going to be. Give us some time. Everybody should have had this experience," he added. "You have to live it to understand it."

Bob talked of a "pervading[9] affection" between the students, the teachers, and Leo and related an example of what he meant. "The girls, when they got old enough, couldn't wear nylons because their hands were too rough from picking cotton. And they had to pick cotton to buy their dresses for the prom. But we understood," he added. "It was part of all of us, what we were and where we were going."

Surely every day was special to the four hundred or so students who attended Weedpatch School. For it was there that they learned a most important lesson: they were as good as anybody else.

9. **pervading** [pər vād′ ing]: spreading everywhere.

JERRY STANLEY

Jerry Stanley was born in 1941 in Highland Park, Michigan. When he was seventeen, Stanley joined the Air Force and was stationed in California. After becoming a civilian again, he finished college and went to graduate school in Arizona—but liked California so much that he moved back. Stanley now teaches history at California State University in Bakersfield. He says he likes driving his motor scooter to work every day.

To research the story of Weedpatch School, Stanley interviewed the school superintendent and principal as well as all the former teachers and students he could locate. *Children of the Dust Bowl* is his first book.

Knoxville, Tennessee

NIKKI GIOVANNI

I always like summer
best
you can eat fresh corn
from daddy's garden
and okra[1]   5
and greens[2]
and cabbage
and lots of
barbecue
and buttermilk   10
and homemade ice-cream
at the church picnic
and listen to
gospel music[3]
outside   15
at the church
homecoming
and go to the mountains with
your grandmother
and go barefooted   20
and be warm
all the time
not only when you go to bed
and sleep

1. **okra** [ō′ krə]: a tall plant with sticky pods used in soups and as a vegetable.
2. **greens:** leaves and stems of plants, such as beets, used for food.
3. **gospel music** [gos′ pəl]: intense, joyful songs about the teachings of Christ and the apostles.

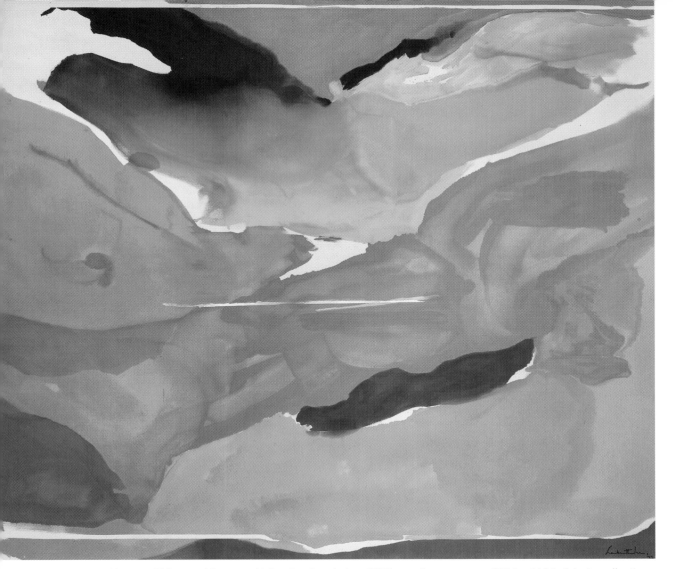

Nature Abhors a Vacuum Helen Frankenthaler, 1973, acrylic on canvas, 103" x 112", Private collection

NIKKI GIOVANNI

Nikki Giovanni was born in 1943 in Knoxville, Tennessee, and grew up there, in the shadow of the Smoky Mountains. In college, Giovanni majored in history and went on to Columbia University School of the Arts. During the civil rights days of the 1960s, she discovered her interest in writing poetry.

Giovanni tells young people, "The older you get, the better you will write. Not just because a writer's skills grow, but because of insight. One isn't born with insight, one obtains it."

Knoxville, Tennessee   **79**

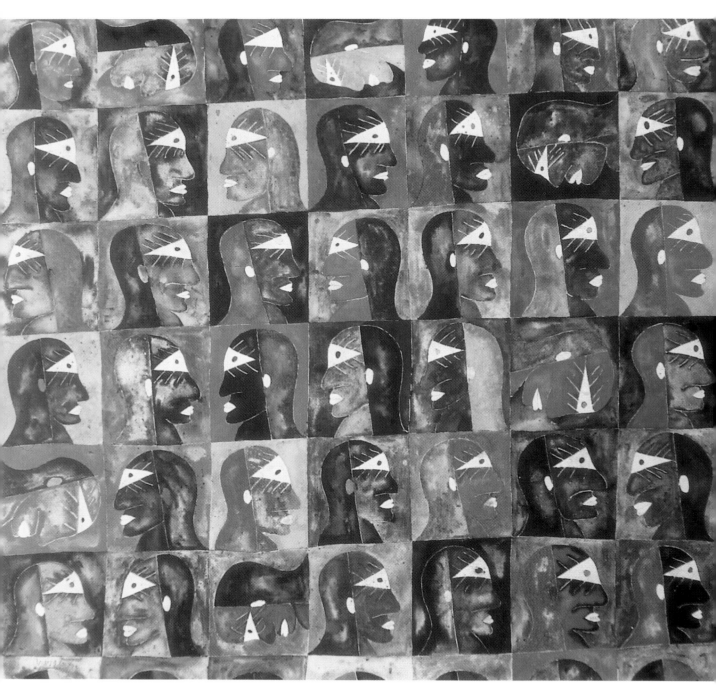

Los Encuentros Javier Arévalo, 1991, Private collection

THOSE WHO DON'T

SANDRA CISNEROS

Those who don't know any better come into our neighborhood scared. They think we're dangerous. They think we will attack them with shiny knives. They are stupid people who are lost and got here by mistake.

But we aren't afraid. We know the guy with the crooked eye is Davey the Baby's brother, and the tall one next to him in the straw brim, that's Rosa's Eddie V. and the big one that looks like a dumb grown man, he's Fat Boy, though he's not fat anymore nor a boy.

All brown all around, we are safe. But watch us drive into a neighborhood of another color and our knees go shakity-shake and our car windows get rolled up tight and our eyes look straight. Yeah. That is how it goes and goes.

SANDRA CISNEROS

Sandra Cisneros was born in 1954 and raised in Chicago. She later went to live in San Antonio, Texas. Calling herself a migrant writer and professor, she has said that her memories of her old neighborhood—the neighborhood of *The House on Mango Street*—move with her, wherever she may live and work.

Cisneros writes both poetry and prose. So far, she has published two books of poems as well as two collections of short stories.

It's All in How

MICKEY ROBERTS

You Say It

Ever since I was a small girl in school, I've been aware of what the school textbooks say about Indians. I am an Indian and, naturally, am interested in what the school teaches about natives of this land.

One day in the grammar school I attended, I read that a delicacy of American Indian people was dried fish, which, according to the textbook, tasted "like an old shoe, or was like chewing on dried leather." To this day I can remember my utter dismay at reading these words. We called this wind-dried fish "sleet-schus," and to us, it was our favorite delicacy and, indeed, did not taste like shoe leather. It took many hours of long and hard work to cure[1] the fish in just this particular fashion. Early fur traders and other non-Indians must have agreed, for they often used this food for subsistence as they traveled around isolated areas.

I brought the textbook home to show it to my father, leader of my tribe at that time. My father was the youngest son of one of the last chiefs of the Nooksack Indian Tribe of Whatcom County in the state of Washington. On this particular day, he told me in his wise and humble manner that the outside world did not always understand Indian people, and that I should not let it hinder me from learning the good parts of education.

1. **cure** [kyùr]: preserve meat or fish by drying, salting, smoking, or pickling.

Woven cup Nooksack tribe, Burke Museum, Seattle, Washington

Since those early years I have learned we were much better off with our own delicacies, which did not rot our teeth and bring about the various dietary problems that plague Indian people in modern times. I was about eight years old when this incident happened and it did much to sharpen my desire to pinpoint terminology in books used to describe American Indian people, books which are, most often, not very complimentary.

At a later time in my life, I had brought a group of Indian people to the county fairgrounds to put up a booth to sell Indian-made arts and crafts. My group was excited about the prospect of making some money selling genuine Indian artifacts. We thanked the man who showed us our booth and told him it was nice of him to remember the people of the Indian community. The man expanded a little and remarked that he liked Indian people. "In fact," he went on to state, "we are bringing some professional Indians to do the show!"

Dish Nooksack tribe, Burke Museum, Seattle, Washington

As we stood there in shock, listening to this uninformed outsider, I looked at my dear Indian companion, an eighty-year-old woman who could well remember the great chiefs of the tribe who once owned all the land of this county before the white man came bringing "civiliza-tion," which in-cluded diseases and pollution. My friend said not a word, but took the hurt as Indian people have done for many years, realizing out-siders are very often tactless and unthinking.

Of course, we all knew that the "professional Indians" were not Indians at all, but dressed in leather and dancing their own dances. And, anyway, how does one become a "professional Indian"?

I remembered my father's words of so long ago and said to my friend as my father had said to me, "They just don't understand Indian people."

Sugar bowl
Nooksack tribe,
Burke Museum,
Seattle, Washington

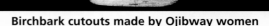
The Forest Cries

IGNATIA BROKER

"When the forest weeps, the Anishinabe[1] who listen will look back at the years. In each generation of Ojibway[2] there will be a person who will hear the si-si-gwa-d,[3] who will listen and remember and pass it on to the children."

I got off the city bus and walked the short one-and-a-half blocks home as I have been doing for years around five o'clock each evening. Because this evening was warm, I walked slower than usual, enjoying the look and feel of the early spring. The earth that had been white was now brown, left uncovered by the melting snow. This brown was turning to green and the air was fragrant with the opening of spring.

Daylight still lingered and as I walked I looked at my neighborhood and thought about it. When I first moved here in the mid-1950s this was a mixed neighborhood of Spanish-speaking people and Catholic whites, and there were many children. Now the Spanish-speaking people are all gone. They left when the parochial school closed its doors, although the church is still here. Now the neighborhood is only four blocks long and two blocks wide, whittled down by urban renewal and the freeways which reach their tentacles all around us.

I reached my doorstep and sat enjoying the good day and remembering the past. It was funny, really, when I think about it. That day thirty years ago when we moved here, me and my children, we were the aliens looking for a place to fit in, looking for a chance of a new life, moving in among these people, some of whose 'forefathers' had

1. **Anishinabe** [ä nish in ä′ bā]: Native Americans of northeast Montana and adjacent parts of Canada, members of the Sioux nation.
2. **Ojibway** [ō jib′ wā]: Native Americans from the region of Lake Superior in the United States and Canada.
3. **si-si-gwa-d** [sē sē qwäd]: the traditional oral story of the Ojibway.

Racing with the Moon Jaune Quick-to-See Smith, 1986, pastel on paper, 30″ x 22″, Private collection

displaced my ancestors for the same reason: looking for a new life. Their fathers were the aliens then, and now they, the children, are in possession of this land.

For a long time I was that Indian person with the two children. But it is good that children have a natural gift of accepting people, and so my children became a part of the neighborhood.

Thirty years in this neighborhood. My children went to school from here, they went to church from here, they were married from here and even though they are in faraway places they seem to have their roots here, for they had lived no other place while growing up.

I talked to my children, even when they were very small, about the ways of the Ojibway people. They were good children and they listened, but I had a feeling that they listened the same as when I read a story about the Bobbsey twins[4] or Marco Polo.[5] I was speaking of another people, removed from them by rock and roll, juvenile singers, and the bobbing movement of the new American dance.

My two, born and raised in Minneapolis, are of that generation of Ojibway who do not know what the reservation[6] means, or the Bureau of Indian Affairs,[7] or the tangled treaties and federal—so called—Indian laws which have spun their webs for a full century around the Native People, the First People of this land.

Now my children are urging me to recall all the stories and bits of information that I ever heard my grandparents or any of the older Ojibway tell. It is important, they say, because now their children are asking them. Others are saying the same thing. It is well that they are asking, for the Ojibway young must learn their cycle.

I have been abroad in this society, the dominating society, for two-thirds of my life, and yet I am a link in a chain to the past. Because of this, I shall do as they ask. I can close my eyes and I am back in the past.

4. **Bobbsey twins:** stories featuring the Bobbsey twins, by Laura Lee Hope.
5. **Marco Polo** [mär′ kō pō′ lō]: Italian merchant of the thirteenth and fourteenth centuries who wrote about his travels in Asia.
6. **reservation** [rez′ ər va′ shən]: place set aside by the government as a place for Native Americans to live.
7. **Bureau of Indian Affairs:** a Civil Service branch related to Native Americans.

I came to the Twin Cities[8] from the reservation in 1941, the year Pearl Harbor was attacked. I went to work in a defense plant and took night classes in order to catch up on the schooling I had missed. I was twenty-two years old and aching for a permanent, settling-down kind of life, but the war years were unstable years for everyone, and more so for the Indian people.

Although employment was good because of the labor demand of the huge defense plants, Indian people faced discrimination in restaurants, night clubs, retail and department stores, in service organizations, public offices, and worst of all, in housing. I can remember hearing, "This room has been rented already, but I got a basement that has a room. I'll show you." I looked at the room. It had the usual rectangular window, and pipes ran overhead. The walls and floors were brown cement, but the man with a gift-giving tone in his voice said, "I'll put linoleum on the floor for you and you'll have a toilet all to yourself. You could wash at the laundry tubs."

There was of course, nothing listed with the War Price and Rationing Board, but the man said it would cost seven dollars a week. I know that he would have made the illegal offer only to an Indian because he knew of the desperate housing conditions we, the first Americans, faced.

I remember living in a room with six others. It was a housekeeping room, nine by twelve feet in size, and meant for one person. It was listed with the price agency at five dollars a week, but the good landlady collected five dollars from each of us each week. However, she did put in a bunk bed and a rollaway which I suppose was all right because we were on different shifts and slept different times anyway. It was cramped and crowded but we had a mutual respect. We sometimes shared our one room with others who had no place, so that there might be nine or ten of us. We could not let friends be out on the street without bed or board. As long as our landlady did not mind, we helped and gave a place of rest to other Ojibway people.

Our paydays were on different days and so whoever had money

8. **Twin Cities:** Minneapolis and the nearby city of St. Paul, Minnesota.

lent carfare and bought meat and vegetables. Stew was our daily fare because we had only a hot plate and one large kettle.

I mention this practice because I know other Indian people did the same thing, and sometimes whole families evolved[9] from it. This was how we got a toehold in the urban areas—by helping each other. Perhaps this is the way nonmaterialistic people do. We were a sharing people and our tribal traits are still within us.

I think now that maybe it was a good thing, the migration of our people to the urban areas during the war years, because there, amongst the millions of people, we were brought to a brotherhood. We Indian people who worked in the war plants started a social group not only for the Ojibway but for the Dakota, the Arikara, the Menominee, the Gros Ventres, the Cree[10], the Oneida[11], and all those from other tribes and other states who had made the trek to something new. And because we, all, were isolated in this dominant[12] society, we became an island from which a revival of spirit began.

It was not easy for any of us during the war years and it became more difficult after the war had ceased. Many Native People returned to the reservations after our soldiers came home from the foreign lands, but others like me stayed and took the buffeting[13] and the difficulties shown us by an alien society.

The war plants closed and people were without jobs. The labor market tightened up and we, the Native People—even skilled workers—faced bias, prejudice, and active discrimination in employment. I know because when I was released from my defense job I answered many advertisements and always I was met with the words, "I'm sorry but we don't hire Indians because they only last the two weeks till payday. Then they quit."

---

9. **evolved** [i volvd′]: developed gradually; here it means that the families moved into the area gradually.
10. **Dakota** [də kō′ tə] **Arikara** [ə rē′ kə rə] **Menominee** [mə nom′ ə nē] **Gros Ventres** [grō vän′ trə] **Cree** [krē] Native Americans, from the northern United States and southern Canada.
11. **Oneida** [ō nī′ də]: Native Americans from central New York State.
12. **dominant** [dom′ ə nənt]: powerful, controlling; here the word refers to those in the area who are not Native American.
13. **buffeting** [buf′ it ing]: the hurts involved in being different.

It was around this time that I met and married a veteran who was passing through to the reservation. He got a job with the railroad. To be close to that job and because of the bias in housing, we moved to the capitol side of the river, to an area of St. Paul called the river flats. It was a poor area. Many of the houses had outdoor toilets; many were but tar-paper shacks. Surprising, but it was so in this very large city. It was here our two children were born and I, like a lot of other Indian women, went out and did day work—cleaning and scrubbing the homes of the middle-income people.

Many Indian families lived on the river flats, which became vibrant with their sharing. People gave to each other because times were bad. No Indian family dared approach the relief and welfare agencies of the Twin Cities. They knew that they would only be given a bus ticket and be told to go back to the reservation where the government would take care of them as usual. This was the policy of the public service agencies, and we put up with it by not asking for the help to which we had a legal right. We also suffered in other ways of their making. My husband was recalled to service and died in Korea. After this I moved from the river flats. I took the clerical training and got my first job at a health clinic.

Because my husband died fighting for a nation designed for freedom for all, I felt that I must help extend that freedom to our people. I joined a group of Indians who had banded together to form an Indian help agency. We built a welfare case to challenge the policy of sending our people back to the reservation, and we were successful. After that, the tide of Indians moving to Minnesota's urban areas increased, and today there are ten thousand of us. As the number grew, new-fangled types of Indian people came into being: those demanding what is in our treaties, those demanding service to our people, those working to provide these services—and all reaching back for identity.

When I see my people every day and know how they are doing, I do not feel so lost in the modern times. The children of our people who come to our agency have a questioning look, a dubious but seeking-to-learn look, and I truly believe that they are reaching back to learn those things of which they can be proud. Many of these children were born and raised in the urban areas and they do not make any distinctions as to their tribes. They do not say, "I am Ojibway," or "I am Dakota," or "I am Arapaho,"[14] but they say, "I am an Indian." Now they, too, are looking to their tribal identity.

These children are again honoring the Old People by asking them to speak, and I like other older people will search my memory and tell what I know. I, myself, shall tell you what I have heard my grandmother tell and I shall try to speak in the way she did and use the words that were hers.

My grandchildren,

I am glad that you, the young Ojibway of today, are seeking to learn the beliefs, the customs, and the practices of our people, for these things have too long been alive only within the memories of the Old Ones. I am glad that you are asking, for it has always been the custom for us to tell what must be passed on so that our ways will be known to the Ojibway children of the future.

Many times when I was a young girl I was fortunate to hear my grandmother tell of the lives and deeds of our grandfathers, grandmothers, and other people of our clan. I listened to these stories, but I really did not know their worth. "What good are these tales in today's world?" asked many people, never realizing that the Ojibway tales teach a philosophy for living. They tell of the purity of man and nature and keeping them in balance.

It is important that you learn the past and act accordingly, for that will assure us that we will always people the earth. I say this because our people who have gone before have said this. They have said that there will be five generations of Ojibway who will make a circle. The first people will start the circle and the others will move from the Ojibway ways. There will be those who will ask questions and those who remember, and the last generation will again act as the Ojibway have acted in years before. Then the circle will be closed.

14. **Arapaho** [ə rap′ ə hō]: Native Americans from Colorado who now live on reservations in Wyoming and Oklahoma.

I do not know which generation the children of today are, but the questions are beginning.

We, the Ojibway, are a forest people. A long time before a strange people came to this country, we lived east and north of this land now called Minnesota in the country of the eastern longhouses. Once we even lived on the big water of salt. We peopled both the north and south banks of what is now called the St. Lawrence River, and by 1770 we reached the north and south shores of what are now called the Great Lakes. We lived in harmony with our kinsmen of the Algonquin nation—the Ottawa, the Menominee, and the Potawatomi[15]—for they, too, were forest peoples. We were the westernmost and perhaps the largest tribe of this nation. The forests were huge and thick, and they were filled with our brethren, the animal people.

We did not own the land acre by acre as is done today, but we respected the right of all people to share in the gifts given by the Great Being to the Anishinabe, which means us, the original people.

The Mi-de-wi-wi-n[16] was a society within all Ojibway communities. Its basic philosophy was the prolonging of life and its practice was the use of herbs, the setting of bones, and the healing of wounds. The use of Mi-de-wi-wi-n rites was restricted to the society's members. They were consulted for their deeper knowledge of medicine.

The gathering and use of herbs was not, however, restricted to the Mi-de-wi-wi-n. Most adult Ojibway had a general knowledge of herbs and medicine, and there were also the Medicine People who had a greater knowledge. This they taught to the younger members of the family so that the practice continued from one generation to the next.

Our family traveled a tortuous path, trying to escape alien contact and retain a satisfying life. As the strange new people, the

---

15. **Algonquin nation** [al gong′ kən]: Native Americans from the valleys of the Ottawa River and northern parts of the St. Lawrence River. **Ottawa** [ot′ ə wə]: Native Americans, part of the Algonquin nation, from the areas around Lake Superior and Lake Huron. **Potawatomi** [pot′ ə wot′ ə mē]: Native Americans of the Algonquin nation from Michigan and Wisconsin.
16. **Mi-de-wi-wi-n** [mē də wē wn]

voyageurs,[17] came into our homeland, pushing and disrupting, many of the Ojibway met with them and became their friends. But our family group preferred to remain in the paths of our ancestors. They moved toward the setting sun and southward to the land of lakes and rivers. They would not deal with the strange people. We, the descendants who now live in the urban areas or on the reservation, have never put a foot in the many places where our ancestors lived, but our roots are in the land of forests where they made their homes.

The best way to learn why we were separated from the first generation is to tell you about the people who lived then. This I shall do by telling you of my great-great-grandmother, who is your grandmother five times removed. Her name was Ni-bo-wi-se-gwe,[18] which means Night Flying Woman. Her nickname was Oona.

The village in which Oona was born was very large and had many lodges. It was north and west of the Lake of Nettles, which is now called Nett Lake, where the A-sa-bi-ig-go-na-ya,[19] the People of the Nettle Fibers, lived. Although Ojibway people had been there many years, they were still thought of as newcomers by the People of the Nettle Fibers. But indeed they had been together a long, long time. They had shared the joy of birth and the sadness of the last journey. They had feasted together in time of plenty and had shared in time of little. They had been happy and there had always been peace among them.

In the early 1800s the strangers, those people who had robbed the white pine from the land of the Cherokee,[20] began looking at the tall trees in the forests of the Ojibway. Soon their clamor reached the communities of the Ojibway. "We need lumber for building homes and ships and the shops in our towns." The industry that ate the forests became king and then the Great White Father, who was de-

17. **voyageurs** [vwä yä zhėr´]: French-Canadian woodsmen, boaters, guides, and workers for early fur-trading companies; the word is French for "travelers."
18. **Ni-bo-wi-se-gwe** [nē bō wē sə gwā]
19. **A-sa-bi-ig-go-na-ya** [ä sä bē ig gō nä yä]
20. **Cherokee** [cher´ ə kē]: Native Americans of the Iroquois nation from the southern Appalachians, now living mostly in Oklahoma.

clared chief of all the people, sent treaty papers to the Ojibway. Six times groups of Ojibway were required to mark the treaties. Each time their lands passed into the hands of the alien peoples, and each group was required to move to a Native Area. These Native Areas are now called the Chippewa[21] reservations of Minnesota.

The strangers rapidly settled in the Ojibway territory. They soon surrounded the Native Areas and ripped away the forests. After them came more strangers who plowed the lands and made the laws and demanded the restriction of the Ojibway to the Native Areas. The council fires burned low because the agents of the strangers now said what must be so and what the Ojibway must do. Then came the peoples with the books, each saying his was the best. They told the Ojibway to mend their ways and follow the words of the book.

This is the time when Oona lived and these were the things that Oona faced. The adjustments that Oona and her family group made were much the same as those made by other family groups. This was the time when the generations of Ojibway began the travel on the circle away from the beginning, clinging in memory to what had been before. What was before must again be there when the circle closes.

21. **Chippewa** [chip′ ə wä]: (Ojibway) Native Americans from the region of Lake Superior in the United States and Canada.

IGNATIA BROKER

Ignatia Broker [1919-1987] was born on the White Earth Indian Reservation in Minnesota.

In 1966, Broker started working with Minneapolis Public Schools to develop an Indian Studies curriculum. She also was head researcher of the Upper Midwest American Indian Center and founder of the Minnesota Indian Historical Society.

Following the example of her mother, who had recorded many of her memories on tape, Broker recorded her own. Her book, *Night Flying Woman,* is based on the life of her great-great-grandmother.

Pittsburgh Memories Romare Beardon, 1984, collage on board, 28 5/8" x 23 1/2"

JEWELL PARKER RHODES

We lived in the dark green hills of Pittsburgh where the smoke from J. L. Steel dusted our clothes gray and blanketed the sky, causing sunsets to streak bright pink and orange. Streetcar wires crisscrossed overhead, making perches for the hungry crows who flew high when the lumbering cars came, spewing electric sparks. Sometimes we'd put pennies in the metal tracks and wait for them to be squashed flat as the streetcars rumbled over them, carrying passengers down the hills into the heart of the city that rested by the three rivers: Ohio, Monongahela, and Allegheny.

But what I remember most about growing up in Pittsburgh was living in a neighborhood where everyone acted like a relative—an aunt, an uncle, a brother, or a sister. Lots of women acted like my mother, bossing me, feeding me. Many would hold me on their laps and tell me stories about High John the Conqueror or John Henry. Some felt no shame about whipping out a comb and fixing my hair when they thought I looked too raggedy. And days when I was lucky, one of my neighborhood mothers would jump in the circle and join me in a waist-twisting, hip-rolling hula-hoop.[1] Sometimes it drove me crazy to have so many mothers, but it also made me feel safe. My real mother was gone—divorced from us—living in another city. But I lived with my dad, my grandparents, an aunt, a sister, and a cousin whom I called sister.

1. **hula-hoop** [hü′ lə hüp′]: a brand name for a ring-shaped, plastic toy that is spun around the hips, introduced in the 1950s.

Dad, Aunt, and Grandpa went off to work while Grandma took care of us. On Tuesdays, she did laundry in the basement and she let us stir the Argo starch and turn the roller drums to wring out all the wet in the clothes. Then we'd help hang the clothes on the line and, when the sheets were dry, she turned a blind eye while we played hide and seek among them. In the house we'd hike to the third floor and slide down the two banisters, smooth and fast, convinced it was better than any roller coaster ride at Kennywood Park.

We had a red tricycle with a bell. My sister, Tonie, had outgrown it. I was just the right size, while cousin Aleta was too small. But when Grandma made chitlins,[2] we would share the bike and make a game of driving through the stinking kitchen while Grandma cleaned out the pig's guts (yuck!) and boiled them. We'd ride our bike through dangerous territory, ringing our bell once we hit the kitchen linoleum, hollering and hooting like "wild ones"—or, as Grandma would say, like "Silly children with no sense!" If you held your nose you couldn't ring the bell and steer at the same time. So we'd count how many bells to figure out who won, who braved the skunky odor and didn't hold their nose the most.

The best part of growing up was the world we saw from our front stoop. Widow Chalmers mothered all the children, watching over us from her porch, waving her fan from the Methodist Church to cool herself in the summer heat. Mr. Berry, who had a splotch of pink roses on his cheek, liked checkers and would roam the street looking for a partner, carrying his own lawn chair. He even played with Aleta, who was five and had to be told every move. There was Jim, who played ball, spinning, ducking and diving, and throwing hoops into a basketball net and would only stop if someone was in any trouble. "Jim, my car stalled." "Jim, can you drive me to the grocery?" "Jim, my sink is clogged." Jim later joined the Army and came home and dunked three baskets in his clod-hopper[3] black shoes and khaki uniform. My sister Tonie, at eleven, swore she'd marry him.

2. **chitlins** [chit′ linz]: the intestines of pigs, cooked as food.
3. **clod-hopper** [klod′ hop′ ər]: strong, heavy shoe.

Detail from **Pittsburgh Memories** Romare Beardon

Stuck-up Rachel liked to cheat at Jacks and had to be black-mailed into playing Double Dutch.[4] "I'll give you some of Grandma's chicken from Sunday dinner," I'd offer. I promised a drumstick for each twenty minutes she turned the rope while I sang and dreamed of winning Double Dutch Champion at the "Y." Truth be told, Grandma would have given anyone who asked a piece of her chicken. Rachel knew it, I knew it. Everyone knew it. But Rachel was two years older than I and, like another big sister, she was nice enough to let me think I was putting one over on her.

Sitting on the steps, looking up and down the block, I saw and felt a world where I was safe, where I knew everybody and everybody knew me. Everybody was brown and black and when babies were born, we'd all wait for them to grow into their skin. Their shades would sometimes grow lighter, sometimes darker. Even the color of their eyes would change—blue became brown, hazel changed to deep green, and brown irises could mellow to a luminous black. Hair textures all varied: soft, bouncy, waves; strands curled in fuzzy, tight spirals; or even hair thick and straight because of a throwback to a Cherokee.[5] I knew we all were beautiful.

Summer block parties were the best. We'd close off traffic and sometimes the Fire Department would open the hydrants and we'd dance and sing while water gushed at us. A spray of wet beneath the moon and stars. Tonie, Aleta, and I pushed boxes together to make a stage and lipsynched to the record player, pretending we were The Supremes. *"Stop, in the name of love! Before you break my heart. Think it o-o-over! . . . "* and we'd giggle as the grown-ups clapped and the other children squealed, and everyone danced, even fat Charlie who could boogie so well you'd swear there was magic in his shoes.

The best block parties happened for no reason. Anyone—even a child—could wake up one day and call for "Block Party Day." And we'd share ribs, corn, chicken, tater pie, and collard greens, and Miss

---

4. **Double Dutch** [dub' əl duch]: a game of jump rope in which two people swing two ropes at the same time, usually in opposite directions.
5. **Cherokee** [cher' ə kē']: Native Americans of the southern Appalachians, now living mostly in Oklahoma.

Sarah who never married always made punch with vanilla ice cream and it would melt into a swishy mess. Finally, when legs wouldn't move another dance step, then the record player was taken away, the street was swept. There were cries and whispers of good night. My real family and I, we'd go into the house. Grandma, Grandpa, Aunt, and Daddy would tuck us in bed and kiss me, Tonie, and Aleta good night. And I would wait until Tonie and Aleta were asleep in the small twin beds (I didn't want them to think I was off my head) and I'd go to the window. Then, peeking over the ledge, I'd whisper my own private "G'night" to the rest of my family, tucked in their beds inside the tall houses all along my street, there in the city where the three rivers meet.

JEWELL   PARKER   RHODES

Jewell Parker Rhodes teaches at Arizona State University in Tempe, Arizona. Despite what she calls her "fondness for gloomy days," she lives with her family in the sunny Arizona desert.

As a child, some of Parker Rhodes's happiest times were block parties. "I loved lipsynching to records," she says, "and I often imagined I'd grow up to become a singer or an actress." Instead, in college she chose to earn degrees in drama criticism, English, and creative writing.

As a writer, Parker Rhodes says, "I can be anything and everything in my imagination." She has written scholarly nonfiction as well as magazine articles, stories, and a novel. She is a co-author of the school book series that includes this literature book.

Asking Big Questions About the Literature

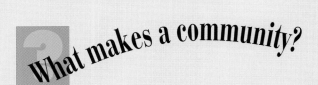

What makes a community?

MAKE A COMMUNITY CHART

How would you define a community? Is it a group of people who share the same surroundings? Do members of a community see each other frequently or share certain responsibilities to their community? Does a community have its own customs like those of a clan or a tribe? Make a chart that shows what makes a community in each literature selection that you read. Use the chart below to help you get started.

Selection Title	Community Features
"Seventh Grade"	Small campus; school routines

LITERATURE STUDY

Setting

The **setting** of a work of fiction is the time and place in which the action occurs. For example, if you wrote a story about life in a community, you would probably want to include details of the neighborhood and the things your characters see every day. These details would be part of the setting.

Choose a fiction selection, such as "Seventh Grade." Write a paragraph describing how the setting helps you imagine when and where the action takes place. (*See "Setting" on page 118.*)

Write a LETTER

Many people get a sense of community from helping others. Imagine that you are Beni Seballos. Write a letter to a newspaper, suggesting ways of helping the sick or homeless in your community.

What communities do people belong to?

LITERATURE STUDY

Theme

In a short story the main idea that the writer wishes to convey is called the **theme**. With a small group, take turns presenting the theme of a short fiction selection from this unit. In other words, what do you think the author is saying about communities? Let your classmates guess the title of the selection you have chosen. (See "Theme" on page 119.)

Create A QUESTIONNAIRE

Discuss the variety of communities described in the literature selections you've read. Then, with a partner, write a survey questionnaire about communities. Ask about the kinds of communities people belong to, how long they have been involved, and so on. Distribute copies of your questionnaire and collect the completed forms. Then write a report about the results. When you have finished your report, compare your results with the communities in the literature in the unit.

CLASSIFY COMMUNITIES

Classifying—grouping together things that have something in common—can help you understand communities. With a partner, list as many kinds of communities as you can—from the literature in this unit and from your own experience. Then decide if each community is a community of *place*, such as a neighborhood, or a community of *culture*, such as the Ojibway. Use a chart like the one here to classify these communities.

Title	Community	Place	Culture
"Block Party"	Neighborhood	X	
"The Forest Cries"	Ojibway		X

Asking Big Questions About the Literature

What responsibilities do people have to their community?

Giving Instructions

Some of the characters in the literature selections in this unit became involved in activities that revealed their sense of community responsibility. For example, in "Beni Seballos," the main character volunteers at a senior citizens center. Look through the literature selections and find an example of such an activity. Then show how it is done. Use a chart like the one below to break the activity down into steps. Present your instructions to the class.

LITERATURE STUDY
Theme

Many of the selections in this unit present the **theme** of responsibility to a community, as in "Empowered to heal." Choose a fiction selection and write an essay discussing the theme of community responsibility in that selection. (*See "Theme" on page 119.*)

Step 1 — Step 2 — Step 3 — Step 4 — Step 5

MAKE
A RESPONSIBILITIES CHART

What responsibilities do the characters in the literature selections have to their communities? For example, in "Empowered to heal," eight teenagers try stop the violence in their communities. Make a chart showing the community responsibilities that you find in each literature selection in this unit.

How do communities change?

Setting

A story's **setting**—its time and place—influences the way its characters behave. With a partner, choose characters from several of the fiction selections in this unit. Discuss the good and bad effects of the setting on each character. Organize this information into a chart like the one below. (*See "Setting" on page 118.*)

Create A DOCUMENTARY

As a group, choose a literature selection from this unit in which a community has experienced some kind of change. Collect information about the historical background of this change. Then present your documentary in the form of a video, an exhibit, or a lecture.

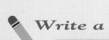 **Write a**

SPEECH

Listen to or read the "I Have a Dream" speech by Martin Luther King, Jr. How would you like to change your community or world? Prepare an "I Have a Dream" speech of your own. Use note cards to practice your speech with a partner. Then give your speech to your classmates. Post a written version of your speech on the bulletin board.

Selection	"The Fun They Had"	
Positive Effects		
Negative Effects	Machines replace school community.	

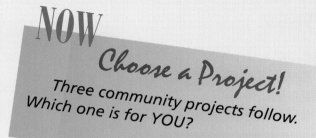 *NOW* **Choose a Project!**
Three community projects follow. Which one is for YOU?

Writing Workshop

A PROPOSAL FOR CHANGE

All communities change. Some may change so slowly that you can't tell they're changing. But sometimes communities change suddenly because people *make* them change—for the better, as in "Empowered to heal," or for the worse, as in "The Forest Cries." In this project, you'll have a chance to propose a change for the better in your own community and explain how this change can be brought about. Maybe you'd like to introduce a recycling program or new bike paths. Haven't you ever declared, "Would I like to do something about *that!*" Well, here's your chance.

First you'll decide *what* you'd like to change. Next you'll decide *how* to change it. Finally you'll write a proposal that explains your plan to an **audience** that might help you make that change.

Since your **purpose** is to explain, you'll need to present the proposal clearly and carefully. If your audience can understand and appreciate your plan, they'll be more likely to carry it out.

Prewriting
GETTING STARTED

If you could change one thing in your community, what would it be? Look around your school, neighborhood, or town. Talk to people; read editorials in local newspapers. What bothers you and others? How might these things be changed? Take notes as you explore. Then write a sentence that clearly states what change you're proposing for the community. This will be the main idea of your proposal.

Planning
YOUR PROPOSAL

After you decide what should be changed in your community, you'll need to plan your project before you start to write. Ask yourself these questions:

- What other information do I need and where can I get it?
- Who is an appropriate audience for my proposal?
- How will the change be brought about?

To help you answer the last question, complete a planning chart like the one below. Remember that you'll have to explain to your audience *how* the change will be brought about.

Tasks	People needed	Supplies	Timing	Expenses

Now think of the procedure that will be necessary to make the change. Break the procedure down into steps that can be easily explained to an audience. Create another chart showing the steps in your procedure for change.

Step 1	
Step 2	
Step 3	

Now that you know what you want to change and how you want to change it, you're ready to draft your proposal.

- Begin with an introductory paragraph that presents the problem that you would like to solve. Jenny Szesterniak, a student writer, introduces her proposal on page 111 with a strong, forceful opening statement: "Our community needs bike paths." Next explain specific ways in which the change would benefit the community. Notice that the rest of Jenny's opening paragraph explains why the community needs these paths and how these paths would improve the quality of life.

- Explain the effects of your proposed change. In her second paragraph, Jenny begins with a topic sentence: "Bike paths would not only be more convenient, they would also be safer . . . . " She then explains how safety would benefit the community.

- Explain how people can bring change about. Give facts, examples, and details. It's easier to convince your audience if they understand how your plan can be carried out. In her third paragraph, Jenny shows what steps to follow to get the support of the whole community. Use your prewriting charts to help you write about the procedure for change.

- Finally write a conclusion. Restate your main idea in different words. Jenny ended her proposal with a final appeal to the community: "Hopefully everyone will realize that bike paths would make life a lot easier and safer."

Remember your purpose—to explain how the change can be brought about—and your audience when you write.

Revising YOUR PROPOSAL

Read your proposal to a writing partner or writing group and get their comments. Also try to read it to someone in the community who might have helped you in the early stages of your project. Do you have a clear topic sentence that expresses your main idea? Did you present the problem clearly? Did you explain the procedure for making the change in clear, logical steps? Do you have a strong concluding sentence?

Editing YOUR PROPOSAL

After you've revised your draft, work with a partner or group to edit your proposal. A final fine tuning will help you win over your audience. Read one another's proposals and check for errors in grammar, spelling, and punctuation. Correct your errors and make a publishable copy of your proposal.

Publishing YOUR PROPOSAL

Be sure your final copy is neat and attractive. Think about adding photos or illustrations.

Mail the proposal, or make an appointment to deliver it yourself. If classmates or friends are your audience, read it aloud or use a copy machine to make copies for everyone. For example, Jenny made a list of groups that might be interested in her proposal, such as the Brookfield Bicycle Club and the P.T.A. of her school. When she had completed her list, Jenny decided which group would be best able to carry out the plan.

Follow up with a note, phone call, or question to find out what people thought. Are they interested in making the change? If so, perhaps you too can be "Empowered to heal"!

A Proposal for Bike Paths

by Jennifer Szesterniak

Brookfield, Wisconsin

Our community needs bike paths. Transportation is very important to our community. Many people who can't drive or don't have a car have a difficult time getting around. Bike paths would make getting around much easier.

Bike paths would not only be more convenient, they would also be safer because cyclists would stop using busy roads. This would help decrease accidents. Adults would like bike paths because they would enjoy riding on them and also feel safer about their children being away from fast-moving cars. Paths would also help people stay physically fit.

We could get bike paths for the city by writing a proposal for the mayor to present to the city council. Then we could plan a publicity campaign to let people know about this problem and gather support. Finally we could survey people to see if they would be willing to support this expense.

Bike paths may sound expensive to build but they are much better than having people's lives endangered by riding on busy roads. Bike paths would also add beauty to the city and keep it on the move in a healthy way. Hopefully everyone will realize that bike paths would make life a lot easier and safer.

Cooperative Learning

A COMMUNITY OF THE FUTURE

"What makes a community?" asks one of the Big Questions in this unit. For this project you'll be asking that question as you work with others to create a model of a community of the future.

The PLAN

With your class, brainstorm a list of futuristic communities, such as a flying school, a floating housing development, a moon colony, an underground mining village, or a fishing village at the bottom of the sea. Then join a group that has chosen to work on one of these communities.

How will you build a model of this community? Decide if you will make a blueprint or a papier-mâché model. Before you build your model, you need to plan. And to plan, you must decide what this community will need.

Brainstorm a list of community wants and needs and sort these into groups. Elect an expert to lead each group, someone who will research his or her subject thoroughly. You may need experts in architecture, science, politics, education, social work, medicine, and so on.

Finally, make a jobs map like the one shown.

FUTURE COMMUNITIES
- Flying school
- Floating City
- Moon town
- underground village

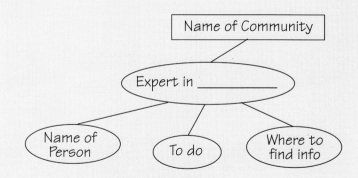

The PROCESS

Now it's time to put your community together. Let each expert present a short research report to the team. Then ask yourselves these questions:

- What needs to be done?
- Who will do it?
- When will it be done?
- What supplies are needed?

Make a planning chart like the one below. Decide who'll perform each task. Then build the future!

Task	Person responsible	What is needed	Date to be done

The PRESENTATION

Before you reveal your community to the world, consider your method of presentation. Provide the model with labels identifying the different parts and functions of your community.

You'll probably want to present your project to your class or school first. Perhaps you can work with the other project teams to create a Futuristic World's Fair. Contact a town official to see if you can display the exhibit in a public building. You might also want to make documentary-style audiotapes about your community.

Consider getting in touch with a community related to yours. Show them what their future might look like!

Helping Your Community

DEVELOPING A PLAN OF ACTION

Remember the Big Question "What responsibilities do people have to their community?" If you believe that people should help their community, then this project may be for you. Your community has needs, and you have talents. Here's a chance to bring them together by developing an action plan for a community project.

Identifying NEEDS

With a partner or a group, brainstorm a list of community needs. How can you help your community? Could you start a Story Hour at the library or pick up litter in the playground?

Use a map like the one below to find ways of meeting your community's needs.

Possible Plans
— Need 1 — Do what? — How? — Where + When?
— Need 2 — Do what? — How? — Where + When?

Before you choose a need for your project, ask yourselves the questions below. Then agree on what you would like to do.

- Is it realistic? Can it really be done?
- Can it be done by people our age?
- Can we complete it in time?
- Is the community likely to want it done?
- Can we get the materials we need?

Drawing Up YOUR PLAN OF ACTION

With your partner or group, decide just how you're going to carry out your project. List the kinds of information you'll need before you can make your plan. Visit and talk to the people involved. Contact officials. Be sure your project is something the community actually *wants*. Keep notes in your journal on everything you do and learn. Here are some of the questions you'll have to ask yourselves.

- Will our project require special permission or permits?
- What materials will be necessary? How will we get them?
- Is any money needed? How much? Where will it come from?
- How many volunteers will be necessary?
- How many people will we be dealing with?
- How will we get the word out? What publicity will we use?

When you have all the information, put your plan together. Use a project chart like the one below.

Steps (in order)	Dates	Materials	Workers
1.			
2.			
3.			

Carrying Out YOUR PLAN OF ACTION

Can you actually carry out your plan of action? Write an introduction, explaining what you would like to do and why. Then add your project chart, adding any explanation that might be helpful. Finally make a neat copy and try sending your plan to the appropriate persons for approval. You might also want to submit a copy to the local newspaper. Who knows what will happen next!

Putting It All Together

What Have You Learned About the Theme?

In this unit, you've thought about many different kinds of communities. How have the literature and activities in this unit affected your ideas about what makes a good community? Look back at the writing you've done for this unit—in your journal, in response to your reading, and in the Writing Workshop. Share your thoughts about community with your classmates by writing an essay, a short story, or a poem about a *Utopian*, or perfect, community. How would such a Utopian community differ from the communities that you know or have read about? Add your writing to a poster of your classmates' writing on the same subject.

A PERFECT COMMUNITY

Prewriting and Drafting   Brainstorm a list of problems facing the modern communities you know or have read about. How would you solve problems such as poverty, pollution, crime, and violence? Is there a way of creating a community in which everyone is happy? Where would such a community be located? Would it be in the city or the country?

Now draft an essay, a short story, or a poem about a perfect, Utopian community. Describe how the people of such a community live without the problems of the modern world and how such a community was created.

Revising and Editing   Work with a writing group or partner. Read your writing aloud to one another. Ask questions that you have about your draft, or ask your partner or group to suggest improvements to the content of your writing. Have your partner check for errors in grammar, punctuation, and spelling too.

Publishing   After you have made your final revisions, rewrite your essay neatly. Add your essay to your classmates' essays. Arrange your essays to fill a bulletin board or a poster with the title "My Utopia."

Evaluating Your Work

Think Back About the Big Questions

Think about the Big Questions on pages 10-11. Discuss your thoughts with a partner, especially your thoughts about questions that still seem hard to answer. Compare your ideas now with your ideas when you started this unit. Record your current thoughts in your journal.

Think Back About Your Work

Now think about the whole unit. What did you do? *How* did you do? To evaluate your work, including your reading, your writing, your activities, and your project, write a note to your teacher. Explain what you've done during this unit and what you've learned. Use the following questions to help you write your note.

- Which literature selections in this unit did you like the most? Why?

- What was your favorite activity in this unit? Why?

- What was your least favorite activity? Why?

- If you were to do your project again, what parts would you do the same way? What parts would you do differently?

- What did you learn as you worked on your project or projects?

- What have you learned in this unit about communities?

- How would you rate your work in this unit? Use the following scale and give at least three reasons for your rating.

1 = Outstanding	3 = Fair
2 = Good	4 = Not as good as it could have been

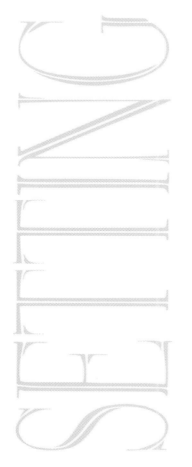

What Is Setting?

Setting is the time and place in which the action of a work of fiction takes place. An author may describe the setting at the beginning of the story or present it through details that appear as the story unfolds. Sometimes the setting dominates the plot. In "Seventh Grade," for example, all the action takes place in a school setting, which is described in great detail. A story's setting may also have an important influence on the story's characters. It can often determine a character's attitudes and way of looking at the world.

Creating a New Setting   Choose one of the fiction selections that you've read in this unit. With a partner, discuss how the setting influences both the main character and the plot of the story. Then try to imagine the selection with a very different setting. How would this affect the main character or the plot of the story? Rewrite the beginning of the story, using a different setting. Then discuss the change with a partner.

A Story Based on Your Life   Write a story based on a real incident in your life or the life of your community, changing the name of your main character so that your story is a work of fiction. Begin the story by describing the setting. Think about the things you see or used to see every day. You might want to scan some of the selections to see how each author introduced the setting of a story. When you have finished your story, present it to the class. See if anyone is familiar with the setting you describe.

What Is Theme?

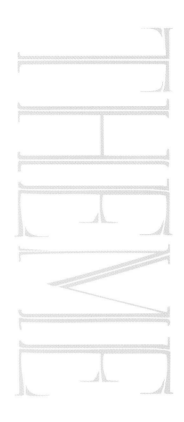

Theme in a piece of literature is the main idea or message that the author wishes to convey. The theme of a story can communicate the writer's attitude or way of looking at the world and can be expressed through setting, plot, or even the words of the characters. In the unit that you have just finished, each selection presented a particular idea or view of community. This idea is the theme. For example, in "The Fun They Had," the story is set in the year 2157, when students will no longer attend school but will be taught individually by machines. The main character, Margie, longs for the time when all the kids met daily in the school community. In this selection, the theme is the importance of community and the warning that one day this community might be lost forever.

Express a Theme Choose a fiction selection that you've read from the unit. Write what you think is the theme of that selection. Then make a list of details and passages that express the main theme. Think of how you could express the same theme in a story or poem of your own. Write your own piece of literature on the theme of community.

Writing a Skit With a partner, choose a theme or message, such as the importance of getting along with your neighbors or the responsibilities of friendship. Then write a short skit or dialogue that expresses that theme. When you have rehearsed your skit, present it to the class.

GLOSSARY OF LITERARY TERMS

A

alliteration   Repetition of the first sound—usually a consonant sound—in several words of a sentence or a line of poetry.

allusion   An author's indirect reference to someone or something that is presumed to be familiar to the reader.

anecdote   A short narrative about an interesting or a humorous event, usually in the life of a person.

antagonist   The person or force opposing the protagonist, or main character in a literary work. [See also *protagonist*.]

autobiography   A person's written account of his or her own life.

B

ballad   A poem, often a song, that tells a story in simple verse.

biography   An account of a person's life, written by another person.

blank verse   Unrhymed poetry.

C

character   A person or an animal that participates in the action of a work of literature. A *dynamic character* is one whose thoughts, feelings, and actions are changeable and lifelike; a *static character* always remains the same. [See also *protagonist*, *antagonist*.]

characterization   The creation of characters through the characters' use of language and through descriptions of their appearance, thoughts, emotions, and actions. [See also *character*.]

chronology   An arrangement of events in the order in which they happen.

cliché   An overused expression that is trite rather than meaningful.

climax   The highest point of tension in the plot of a work of literature. [See also *plot*.]

comedy   An amusing play that has a happy ending.

conclusion   The final part or ending of a piece of literature.

concrete poem   A poem arranged on the page so that its punctuation, letters, and lines make the shape of the subject of the poem.

conflict   A problem that confronts the characters in a piece of literature. The conflict may be *internal* (a character's struggle within himself or herself) or *external* (a character's struggle against nature, another person, or society). [See also *plot*.]

context   The general sense of words that helps readers to understand the meaning of unfamiliar words and phrases in a piece of writing.

D

description   An author's use of words to give the reader or listener a mental picture, an impression, or an understanding of a person, place, thing, event, or idea.

dialect   A form of speech spoken by people in a particular group or geographical region that differs in vocabulary, grammar, and pronunciation from the standard language.

dialogue   The spoken words and conversation of characters in a work of literature.

drama   A play that is performed before an audience according to stage directions and using dialogue. Classical drama has two genres: *tragedy* and *comedy*. Modern drama includes *melodrama*, *satire*, *theater of the absurd*, and *pantomime*. [See also *comedy*, *play*, and *tragedy*.]

dramatic poetry   A play written in the form of poetry.

E

epic   A long narrative poem—written in a formal style and meant to be read aloud—that relates the adventures and experiences of one or more great heroes or heroines.

essay   Personal nonfiction writing about a particular subject that is important to the writer.

excerpt   A passage from a larger work that has been taken out of its context to be used for a special purpose.

exposition   Writing that explains, analyzes, or defines.

extended metaphor   An elaborately drawn out metaphor. [See also *metaphor*.]

F

fable   A short, simple story whose purpose is to teach a lesson, usually with animal characters who talk and act like people.

fantasy   Imaginative fiction about unrealistic characters, places, and events.

fiction   Literature, including the short story and the novel, that tells about imaginary people and events.

figurative language   Language used to express ideas through figures of speech: descriptions that aren't meant to be taken literally. Types of figurative language include *simile, metaphor, extended metaphor, hyperbole,* and *personification*.

figure of speech   A type of figurative language, not meant to be taken literally, that expresses something in such a way that it brings the thing to life in the reader's or listener's imagination. [See also *figurative language*.]

flashback   A break in a story's action that relates a past happening in order to give the reader background information about a present action in the story.

folktale   A story that has been passed along from storyteller to storyteller for generations. Kinds of folktales include *tall tales, fairy tales, fables, legends,* and *myths*.

foreshadowing   The use of clues to create suspense by giving the reader or audience hints of events to come.

free verse   Poetry that has no formal rhyme scheme or metrical pattern.

G

genre   A major category of art. The three major literary genres are poetry, prose, and drama.

H

haiku   A three-line Japanese verse form. In most haiku, the first and third lines have five syllables, while the second line has seven. The traditional haiku describes a complicated feeling or thought in simple language through a single image.

hero/heroine   The main character in a work of literature. In heroic literature, the hero or heroine is a particularly brave, noble, or clever person whose achievements are unusual and important. [See also *character*.]

heroic age   The historical period in western civilization—from about 800 B.C. through A.D. 200—during which most works of heroic literature, such as myths and epics, were created in ancient Greece and Rome.

hubris   Arrogance or excessive pride leading to mistakes; the character flaw in a hero of classical tragedy.

hyperbole   An obvious exaggeration used for emphasis. [See also *figurative language*.]

I

idiom   An expression whose meaning cannot be understood from the ordinary meaning of the words. For example, *It's raining cats and dogs*.

imagery   The words and phrases in writing that appeal to the senses of sight, hearing, taste, touch, and smell.

irony An effect created by a sharp contrast between what is expected and what is real. An *ironic twist* in a plot is an event that is the complete opposite of what the characters have been hoping or expecting will happen. An *ironic statement* declares the opposite of the speaker's literal meaning.

J

jargon Words and phrases used by a group of people who share the same profession or special interests in order to refer to technical things or processes with which they are familiar. In general, jargon is any terminology that sounds unclear, overused, or pretentious.

L

legend A famous folktale about heroic actions, passed along by word of mouth from generation to generation. The legend may have begun as a factual account of real people and events but has become mostly or completely fictitious.

limerick A form of light verse, or humorous poetry, written in one five-line stanza with a regular scheme of rhyme and meter.

literature The branch of art that is expressed in written language and includes all written genres.

lyric poem A short poem that expresses personal feelings and thoughts in a musical way. Originally, lyrics were the words of songs that were sung to music played on the lyre, a stringed instrument invented by the ancient Greeks.

M

metamorphosis The transformation of one thing, or being, into another completely different thing or being, such as a caterpillar's change into a butterfly.

metaphor Figurative language in which one thing is said to be another thing. [See also *figurative language*.]

meter The pattern of rhythm in lines of poetry. The most common meter, in poetry written in English, is iambic pentameter, that is, a verse having five metrical feet, each foot of verse having two syllables, an unaccented one followed by an accented one.

mood The feeling or atmosphere that a reader senses while reading or listening to a work of literature.

motivation A character's reasons for doing, thinking, feeling, or saying something. Sometimes an author will make a character's motivation obvious from the beginning. In realistic fiction and drama, however, a character's motivation may be so complicated that the reader discovers it gradually, by studying the character's thoughts, feelings, and behavior.

myth A story, passed along by word of mouth for generations, about the actions of gods and goddesses or superhuman heroes and heroines. Most myths were first told to explain the origins of natural things or to justify the social rules and customs of a particular society.

N

narration The process of telling a story. For both fiction and nonfiction, there are two main kinds of narration, based on whether the story is told from a first-person or third-person point of view. [See also *point of view*.]

narrative poem A poem that tells a story containing the basic literary ingredients of fiction: character, setting, and plot.

narrator The person, or voice, that tells a story. [See also *point of view, voice*.]

nonfiction Prose that is factually true and is about real people, events, and places.

nonstandard English
Versions of English, such as slang and dialects, that use pronunciation, vocabulary, idiomatic expressions, grammar, and punctuation that differ from the accepted "correct" constructions of English.

novel   A long work of narrative prose fiction. A novel contains narration, a setting or settings, characters, dialogue, and a more complicated plot than a short story.

O

onomatopoeia   The technique of using words that imitate the sounds they describe, such as *hiss*, *buzz*, and *splash*.

oral tradition   Stories, poems, and songs that have been kept alive by being told, recited, and sung by people over many generations. Since the works were not originally written, they often have many different versions.

P

parable   A brief story—similar to a fable, but about people—that describes an ordinary situation and concludes with a short moral or lesson to be learned.

personification   Figurative language in which an animal, an object, or an idea is given human characteristics. [See also *figurative language*.]

persuasion   A type of speech or writing whose purpose is to convince people that something is true or important.

play   A work of dramatic literature written for performance by actors before an audience. In classical or traditional drama, a play is divided into five acts, each containing a number of scenes. Each act represents a distinct phase in the development of the plot. Modern plays often have only one act and one scene.

playwright   The author of a play.

plot   The sequence of actions and events in fiction or drama. A traditional plot has at least three parts: the *rising action*, leading up to a turning point that affects the main character; the *climax*, the turning point or moment of greatest intensity or interest; and the *falling action*, leading away from the conflict, or resolving it.

poetry   Language selected and arranged in order to say something in a compressed or nonliteral way. Modern poetry may or may not use many of the traditional poetic techniques that include *meter*, *rhyme*, *alliteration*, *figurative language*, *symbolism*, and *specific verse forms*.

point of view   The perspective from which a writer tells a story. *First-person* narrators tell the story from their own point of view, using pronouns such as *I* or *me*. *Third-person* narrators, using pronouns such as *he*, *she*, or *them*, may be *omniscient* (knowing everything about all characters), or *limited* (taking the point of view of one character). [See also *narration*.]

propaganda   Information or ideas that may or may not be true, but are spread as though they are true, in order to persuade people to do or believe something.

prose   The ordinary form of written and spoken language used to create fiction, nonfiction, and most drama.

protagonist   The main character of a literary work. [See also *character* and *characterization*.]

R

refrain   A line or group of lines that is repeated, usually at the end of each verse, in a poem or a song.

repetition   The use of the same formal element more than once in a literary work, for emphasis or in order to achieve another desired effect.

resolution   The falling action in fiction or drama,

including all of the developments that follow the climax and show that the story's conflict is over. [See also *plot*.]

rhyme scheme   A repeated pattern of similar sounds, usually found at the ends of lines of poetry or poetic drama.

rhythm   In poetry, the measured recurrence of accented and unaccented syllables in a particular pattern. [See also *meter*.]

S

scene   The time, place, and circumstances of a play or a story. In a play, a scene is a section of an act. [See also *play*.]

science fiction   Fantasy literature set in an imaginary future, with details and situations that are designed to seem scientifically possible.

setting   The time and place of a work of literature.

short story   Narrative prose fiction that is shorter and has a less complicated plot than a novel. A short story contains narration, at least one setting, at least one character, and usually some dialogue.

simile   Figurative language that compares two unlike things, introduced by the words "like" or "as." [See also *figurative language*.]

soliloquy   In a play, a short speech spoken by a single character when he or she is alone on the stage. A soliloquy usually expresses the character's innermost thoughts and feelings, when he or she thinks no other characters can hear.

sonnet   A poem written in one stanza, using fourteen lines of iambic pentameter. [See also *meter*.]

speaker   In poetry, the individual whose voice seems to be speaking the lines. [See also *narration, voice*.]

stage directions   The directions, written by the playwright, to tell the director, actors, and theater technicians how a play should be dramatized. Stage directions may specify such things as how the setting should appear in each scene, how the actors should deliver their lines, when the stage curtain should rise and fall, how stage lights should be used, where on the stage the actors should be during the action, and when sound effects should be used.

stanza   A group of lines in poetry set apart by blank lines before and after the group; a poetic verse.

style   The distinctive way in which an author composes a

work of literature in written or spoken language.

suspense   An effect created by authors of various types of fiction and drama, especially adventure and mystery, to heighten interest in the story.

symbol   An image, person, place, or thing that is used to express the idea of something else.

T

tall tale   A kind of folk tale, or legend, that exaggerates the characteristics of its hero or heroine.

theme   The main idea or underlying subject of a work of literature.

tone   The attitude that a work of literature expresses to the reader through its style.

tragedy   In classical drama, a tragedy depicts a noble hero or heroine who makes a mistake of judgment that has disastrous consequences.

V

verse   A stanza in a poem. Also, a synonym for poetry as a genre. [See also *stanza*.]

voice   The narrator or the person who relates the action of a piece of literature. [See also *speaker*.]

ACKNOWLEDGMENTS

Grateful acknowledgment is made for permission to reprint the following copyrighted material.

"Seventh Grade" from *Baseball in April and Other Stories* by Gary Soto, copyright ©1990 by Gary Soto, reprinted by permission of Harcourt Brace and Company.

"They think I'm an expert" by Catherine Crocker is reprinted by permission of the Associated Press.

From *The Diary of Latoya Hunter* by Latoya Hunter. Copyright ©1992 by Latoya Hunter. Reprinted by permission of Crown Publishers, Inc.

"Empowered to heal" by Michael Grunwald from *The Boston Globe*, April 22, 1993. Reprinted by courtesy of *The Boston Globe*.

"Break a Leg" by Joel Schwartz. Copyright © 1992 by Joel Schwartz, from *Funny You Should Ask* by David Gale, Editor. Used by permission of Dell Books, a division of Bantam Doubleday Dell Publishing Group, Inc.

"Founders of the Children's Rain Forest" from *It's Our World Too!* by Phillip Hoose. Copyright © 1993 by Phillip Hoose. By permission of Little, Brown and Company.

"Beni Seballos" from *It's Our World Too!* by Phillip Hoose. Copyright © 1993 by Phillip Hoose. By permission of Little, Brown and Company.

"The Fun They Had" by Isaac Asimov from *Earth Room is Enough* by Isaac Asimov. Copyright © 1957 by Isaac Asimov. Used by permission of Doubleday, a division of Bantam Doubleday Dell Publishing Group, Inc.

"Something to Watch" and "Our School" from *Children of the Dust Bowl* by Jerry Stanley. Copyright © 1992 by Jerry Stanley. Reprinted by permission of Crown Publishers, Inc.

"Knoxville, Tennessee" by Nikki Giovanni from *Ego Tripping and Other Poems for Young Readers*. Copyright © 1973 by Nikki Giovanni. By permission of the author.

"Those Who Don't" from *The House On Mango Street* by Sandra Cisneros. Copyright © 1989 by Sandra Cisneros. Published in the United States by Vintage Books, a division of Random House, Inc., New York, and distributed in Canada by Random House of Canada Limited, Toronto. Originally published by Arte Publico Press in somewhat different form in 1984 and revised in 1989. Reprinted by permission of Susan Bergholz Literary Services, New York.

"It's All In How You Say It" by Mickey Roberts, from *Talking Leaves*, edited by Craig Lesley, copyright © 1991 by Craig Lesley. By permission of Dell Publishing, a division of Bantam Doubleday Dell Publishing Group, Inc.

"The Forest Cries" by Ignatia Broker, reprinted from *Night Flying Woman: An Ojibway Narrative* by Ignatia Broker, copyright © 1983 by the Minnesota Historical Society.

"Block Party" by Jewell Parker Rhodes, copyright © 1993 by Jewell Parker Rhodes, is reprinted by permission of the author.

ILLUSTRATION

36-41 Peter Horjus.

PHOTOGRAPHY

4 *l* John Owens/©D.C. Heath; *r* Sarah Putnam/©D.C. Heath; 5 Michael Fogden/DRK Photo; 6 Julie Bidwell/©D.C. Heath; 8 *t* Bob Daemmrich/Stock Boston; *b* Elizabeth Zuckerman/PhotoEdit; 9 *t* Bob Daemmrich/Stock Boston; *b* Kolvoord/The Image Works; 10 *l* Sarah Putnam/©D.C. Heath; *r* Sandy Roessler/The Stock Market; 11 *t* Skjold/The Image Works; *c* Jim Whitmer/Stock Boston; *b* Mary Kate Denny/PhotoEdit; 12, 18 Carol Palmer/©D.C. Heath; 19 Photo by Caroline Soto; 20 Porter Gifford/Gamma Liaison; 24-25, 26-31 *border* Curtis Willocks/Brooklyn Image Group; 31 Courtesy of Crown Publishers, Inc.; 33 Shayna Brennan/AP; 41 Courtesy of Bantam Doubleday Dell; 42-43 Gary Braasch; 43 Courtesy of Bernd W. Kern/The Children's Rain Forest of Sweden; 44 Michael Fogden/Animals Animals/Earth Scenes; 44-53 *border* Gary Braasch; 47 John Cancalosi/DRK Photo; 48, 51 Michael Fogden/DRK Photo; 52 Courtesy of The Children's Rain Forest of Sweden; 53 Photo by Richard Connelly; 54 *tl, tr, b* Joel Gordon; 54 *inset,* 55-61 *background* H.D. Thoreau/Westlight; 60 Jennifer Appleton; 61 Photo by Richard Connelly; 62-63, 64-65 *background* Jook Leung Photography; 65 *inset* AP/Wide World Photos; 66-67 U.S. Department of Agriculture Soil Conservation Service/The Oklahoma Historical Society; 68, 69, 71, 72, 76 Courtesy of Jerry Stanley; 68-77 *background* U.S. Department of Agriculture Soil Conservation Service/The Oklahoma Historical Society; 77 *inset* Photo by Joe Bariffi/Courtesy of Random House, Inc.; 79 *t* Private Collection, New York. Courtesy Andre Emmerich Gallery; *b* Photo by Jill Oxendine; 80 Private Collection, Iturralde Gallery, Los Angeles, CA; 81 AP/Wide World Photos; 82-85 Courtesy of the Burke Museum, Seattle, WA; 86 Steinbaum Krauss Gallery, New York, NY; 87-95 *top border* National Anthropological Archives, Smithsonian Institution, Washington, D.C. 596-E-48; 95 *b* Staff photo by Darlene Pfister/*Star Tribune*, Minneapolis and St. Paul, MN; 96, 99 Museum of Art, The Carnegie Institute, Pittsburgh, PA. Gift of Mr. and Mrs. Ronald R. Davenport and Mr. and Mrs. Milton A. Washington. 84.63; 104 Nancy Sheehan/©D.C. Heath; 106 *t* Elizabeth Hamlin/Stock Boston; *b* Alan McClennen, Jr.; 110 Mark C. Flannery; 111 Jonathan Stoke/Rails-to-Trails; 112 Jean-Claude LeJeune/Stock Boston; 113 Masahiro Sano/The Stock Market; 114 *t* J. Sulley/The Image Works; *b* Bob Daemmrich/Stock Boston.

Back cover *t* Sarah Putnam/©D.C. Heath; *c* Julie Bidwell/©D.C. Heath; *b* Jim Whitmer/Stock Boston.

Full Pronunciation Key for Footnoted Words

(Each pronunciation and definition is adapted from *Scott, Foresman Advanced Dictionary* by E.L. Thorndike and Clarence L. Barnhart.)

The pronunciation of each footnoted word is shown just after the word, in this way: **abbreviate** [ə brē′ vē āt]. The letters and signs used are pronounced as in the words below. The mark ′ is placed after a syllable with primary or heavy accent, as in the example above. The mark ′ after a syllable shows a secondary or lighter accent, as in **abbreviation** [ə brē′ vē ā′ shən].

Some words, taken from foreign languages, are spoken with sounds that do not otherwise occur in English. Symbols for these sounds are given in the key as "foreign sounds."

a	hat, cap	j	jam, enjoy	u	cup, butter	**foreign sounds**
ā	age, face	k	kind, seek	ù	full, put	
ä	father, far	l	land, coal	ü	rule, move	Y as in French *du*.
		m	me, am	v	very, save	Pronounce (ē) with
b	bad, rob	n	no, in	w	will, woman	the lips rounded as
ch	child, much	ng	long, bring	y	young, yet	for (ü).
d	did, red			z	zero, breeze	
		o	hot, rock	zh	measure, seizure	à as in French *ami*.
e	let, best	ō	open, go			Pronounce (ä) with
ē	equal, be	ô	order, all	ə represents:		the lips spread and
ėr	term, learn	oi	oil, voice		a in about	held tense.
		ou	house, out		e in taken	
f	fat, if				i in pencil	œ as in French *peu*.
g	go, bag	p	paper, cup		o in lemon	Pronounce (ā) with the
h	he, how	r	run, try		u in circus	lips rounded as for (ō).
		s	say, yes			
i	it, pin	sh	she, rush			N as in French *bon*.
ī	ice, five	t	tell, it			The N is not pro-
		th	thin, both			nounced, but shows
		ᴦH	then, smooth			that the vowel before
						it is nasal.
						H as in German *ach*.
						Pronounce (k) without
						closing the breath
						passage.